D0359688

THE
AMERICANS
ARE COMING!!!
THE LAST HOPE TO END THE WAR IN HOLLAND

BY
DIRK VAN LEENEN

The American's Are Coming
by Dirk van Leenen

Printed in the United States of America

ISBN 978-1-58588-997-6 Paperback
978-1-58588-998-3 Hardcover

Edited by: Tammy Zubeck and Louise Lindley
Cover Design and Layout: Image Legends, LLC

lifehouse@cox.net

DEDICATION AND THANKS

I am dedicating this second book on World War Two in The Netherlands to those who can no longer read it, all those Resistance people in Holland who have passed away. But also to those Resistance people who are now too old to read a book. I know they wanted to relate this story to the world. I am thankful to have been able to do it for them.

I am also dedicating this book to my two daughters who have passed away from cancer in the last three years. They too are no longer able to read this story.

I thank my loving wife Cindy who encouraged and tolerated me to be by myself in a room, alone with my thoughts and my computer.

I thank Louise Lindley for editing some of my clumsy sentences, and Larry Walker for the creation of the cover.

I thank all the readers who have purchased my first book " Resistance on a Bicycle". They clearly inspired me to keep going in order to finish this second book.

A WORD FROM THE AUTHOR

This book begins where my first book Resistance on a Bicycle left off.

When the Canadians landed in September of 1944 all the citizens danced in the streets and the Germans in the East fled to their Heimat, loaded with their loot.

The most difficult time of the war began and for eight months new Nazis fought harder and meaner to get the population under control. Despite their ruthlessness they never really succeeded because of the determination of the Dutch Resistance.

There is much more to relate, the hundreds of stories from Resistance fighters and citizens are too many, some too personal and others too painful to tell.

A common misunderstanding needs to be explained: The word Holland is not really the name of the country. It is the name of the two most eastern provinces of The Netherlands, which is the proper name of the country. The word Dutch is often thought to be the same as Deutsch. It is not, of course. Dutch is the language of The Netherlands while Deutsch is the Language of Germany.

I have written a glossary of the Dutch and German words at the end of this book, so that a full understanding can be achieved about these heart wrenching stories.

It all happened in real life, which is why my motto "lest we forget" is of the utmost importance in a time when even world leaders dare to deny the Holocaust ever happened.

Wishing you a great reading experience,
The Author, Dirk van Leenen

TABLE OF CONTENTS

TABLE OF CONTENTS

Chapter One

UNCONQUERABLE PEOPLE

"This is the BBC, Radio Oranje.

The Allied forces are in the Ardennes confronting heavy resistance from Rommel and his tank brigades. 'Heavy casualties occur on both sides of the front,' General Eisenhower reported today in a press conference. We are making progress but it is with great difficulty and at too much cost. A message for our friends in Holland: City three can expect a parcel at 1900; make sure the light goes on at this hour and have at least 10 standbys to receive the package, estimated at 400 pounds. Long live the Queen."

The four men in the shelter beneath the house of Kees van Rijn had listened to the message on their crackling hidden radio. It was a radio that had been carefully kept from the soldiers whenever they had searched the house at the Deiman Straat. Frans looked at his old chain watch as he rose up from the sandy floor and exclaimed, "We better get ready to go! It is six o'clock and who knows how long it will take us to get there if we run into a roadblock or a Nazi patrol."

Each of the four men left at a different time. Each of them had a task to do. They had to notify four others to come to the drop site within the hour, and, of the ones who were notified, two others had to get the message out to the last of the ten resistance fighters.

For Kees this kind of "work" was new, but since each of the men were hoping the end of the war was in sight, they all had to change their kind of "work" and adjust it to the present situation.

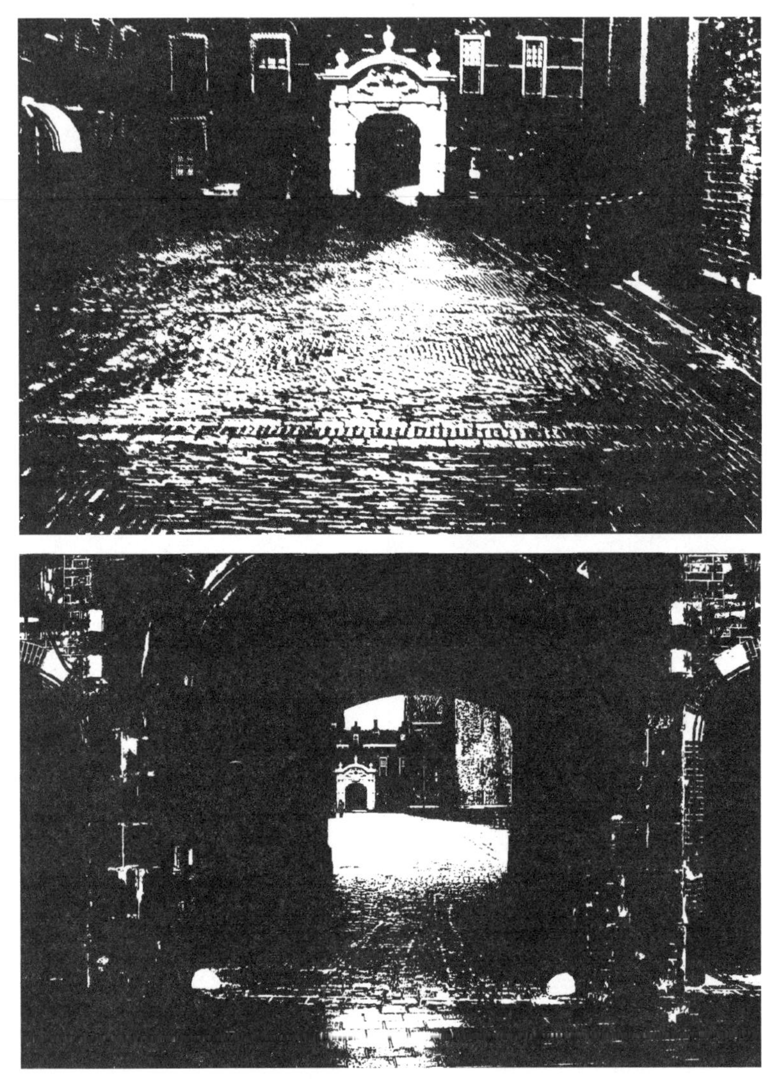

The ancient Binnenhof from where the Nazis ruled.

For Kees, the change entailed having fewer people under the floor of his house, fewer trips to deliver Jews to the hiding places and fewer fake distribution stamps to distribute. He was still the number one man supplying fake ID's, a job that he had refined to perfection together with his son Cornelius.

The new work involved the pick-up of dropped shipments by the British Air force consisting mainly of weaponry and ammunition. The shipments also included German Uniforms and, above all, the much needed food.

Another aspect of the new work was the rescue of Allied pilots who were shot down by the Germans. They were in grave danger when they had to parachute out of their downed planes. If they were not picked up by the Resistance quickly enough, they would end up in a prisoner of war camp. Often worse than that, they could end up with a bullet from the ruthless Nazi-Hitler Juegent army that at that time was occupying the country of The Netherlands.

It was a pitch-dark night on that fall evening, good for a dropping and even better for ten men to go to a field right next to the airport outside of The Hague. They had to cross the river *Vliet* on a secret pond that was hidden close to the bridge and out of the vision of the Nazi Guards on top of the bridge. The men all went on their own, keeping a distance from each other just in case they were seen by a German patrol.

The field used to be a meadow in which hundreds of cows would find their daily dinner in exchange for a twice-daily bucket of milk. Alas, the cows were gone; confiscated by the Nazis and shipped to their homeland to feed the hungry German wives and children of the soldiers. The farmer himself who had owned the cows had been shipped off to work in the Nazi war industry. The field was surrounded by twiggy pussy willow bushes.

The grass had grown wild and mixed with tall weeds and was an ideal place for illegal droppings. It had been used several times and each time the job was done quickly and efficiently, and the Resistance men had safely disappeared when the Nazis arrived.

The ten men each knew their task; each of them had a half liter bottle of gasoline hidden under his trench coat. They all had a box of matches and a small piece of newspaper in their pockets. Before they had left their homes, they had synchronized their watches by the clock of the BBC. At two minutes before seven they all heard the low humming sound of the airplane coming from the West. It was flying low as if it were going to land at the airport. The men were ready, their bottles of gasoline in their hands, the piece of paper was on the ground, the box of matches nearby and one or two matches on top of the box. The plan had been rehearsed several times. When the noise of the engines grew louder and louder it was as if the men heard a command, but none was given. The bottles were emptied and on a one, two, three, four, five count, all ten matches struck the matchbox. Ten flames lit the night sky for just half a minute; and then it was dark again. They could hear the muffled thuds of packages falling on the ground. Then the plane accelerated and rose sharply into the night sky.

As usual, the German searchlights lit up the dark sky. But, before they could even shoot their anti aircraft guns, the plane had disappeared, too high for the flak to hit it.

The ten men had already picked up the cargo and ran to the far end of the field when they heard the sound of the motor cycles and the screeching sound of the gate being opened. The saw the lights of the motor cycles racing towards the center of the field. The soldiers were screaming at each other. Kees heard one of them yell, “Nieghts loess” (Nothing going on). The pick-up crew remained flat on their faces for what seemed a long time and finally the motor cycles returned through the gate from which they came.

The cargo had arrived safely this time and without any casualties. The ten Dutchmen knew why; these German soldiers had been at the airport for four years and as a result they were not very fanatical. They were the same ones who had been at the airport from the beginning of the war without any serious incidents. They wanted to stay out of the limelight and were more concerned for their safety than anything else.

The most dangerous part of their mission had just begun. They had to carry their contraband cargo to their homes. Each man had to carry about 40 pounds; some were parts of a machine gun and others were packets of machine gun ammunition. All of it was heavy and too big to hide under their large black trench coats. They had split up, each going his own separate way and pace, through back yards and alleys, hauling their cargo over fences and through ditches. In spite of the danger and difficulties, they all safely reached their homes. This time it was without incident, which was very rare under the circumstances.

The Nazis could never win a war against the Dutch whose underground army encompassed the entire population except for the comparative small number of collaborators. Those traitors were gradually disappearing from the war scene. Knowing the end was in sight, many of them were moving to Germany thinking they would be safe there.

Daily messages of hope came from the BBC, Radio Oranje, named after the House of Orange, dating back to the time when Willem of Orange established his kingdom in The Netherlands. The royal family reigned from England and was in close contact with the Resistance.

Communication during the last year of the war gradually improved as the Nazis saw the end of the war coming. Daily broadcast from Radio Oranje included constant messages for the Resistance and the local Dutch authorities. Those Dutch authorities did not have any power in the eyes of the Nazi commanders, but they did control the Resistance and were involved in the preparations for the final capitulation of the Hitler clan.

The Yankees are on their way. It was the most heard sentence during the last six months of the war. It was interesting that the Dutch almost always referred to the Allied Liberation Forces which were fighting their way into the countries of Europe as “The Yankees.” In reality the Forces included the military strength of several other countries who were rarely mentioned. Yet it was the British, commonly called the Tommies, and the Canadians, who actually liberated the country.

Kees and Frans arrived home at the same time. They were exhausted from hauling the heavy cargo; both men had no idea what they had carried or what to do with it. They knew that that night, or the next, the fighting men of the Resistance would find their way to the different locations to collect the cargo. That too, was directed from the Headquarters in England, where the preparations were well underway to recapture the country once the Nazis surrendered.

"To the west and south of the country the big cities are evacuated," Frans told Kees when they sat down and enjoyed a cup of surrogate coffee. "The Americans are planning to invade the south any day now, so it will soon be over."

"I would not count on it too soon, Frans," Kees replied, "The Nazis are reinforcing their troops and their equipment and are digging in for a big fight."

" I know they are, but don't you think the soldiers are sick of the war and hoping someone will kill Hitler one of these days and then it will be over? There has been another attack on Hitler and Himmler just yesterday. The Generals in charge thought they had killed them, but when the smoke settled, Hitler and his cronies were still alive and kicking. The SS is now arresting all the culprits and shooting them on sight. I have heard it on the German Radio." Frans had a better radio in his state-of-the-art basement. Since he spoke German fluently, he listened to Radio Berlin everyday to see if he could make any sense of the Nazi troop movements.

"The Americans are coming," Kees said it every day. The thought gave him hope; the only hope there was at the worst time in history for the Dutch. The news was erratic and each day more controversial news was spread. Sometimes the German soldiers gave information to the citizens who were forced to work for them, in hopes it would be spread amongst the population. Often it was misinformation designed to confuse the citizens.

It was late in the evening that early October day in 1944 when the two friends decided to go down to the hiding place under the floor of the house.

"At twelve o'clock there will be a special radio broadcast from the BBC," Kees announced, "and we should make sure to listen to all possible news we can get a hold of, so we can inform the *group* of any and all developments in regards to the advancements of the Allieds." The 'group' was a circle of Resistance people in the neighborhood). Five minutes later both friends were sitting in the sand underneath their city home.

"This is the BBC, Radio Oranje, with news from the front lines. This morning the Allied troops have reached the City of Terneuzen in Zeeland. Like Moses, when he had his back against the Red Sea, the Liberation Forces face the River Schelde."

Hundreds of pontoons were being prepared to cross the river, which at this time was wider than the Red Sea. "The Allieds have commanded the citizens of the Zeeland Isles to evacuate because bombing of the German positions will begin early tomorrow morning. The citizens are urged to leave immediately because there will be no shelters against the barrage of bombs. Heavy fighting is reported in all the southern cities and where the Allieds have not yet arrived. The Nazis are looting every house and shop taking anything of value and shipping it to Germany. Reports have shown long lines of German vehicles loaded with furniture, tools, farm equipment and musical instruments. The Nazis are cleaning out every building systematically, leaving nothing behind. The ultimate shameless act is that they place large banners on the looted shipments stating: *Liebesgaben aus Holland* (Love gifts from Holland).

"The citizens in the liberated areas are warned to obey the commands of the Allieds until further order. The citizens of the occupied areas are warned to wait patiently for the liberators. Electricity may be turned off in the coming days and the use of tap water may become limited. Citizens in the occupied territories are urged to store water while they can.

"This is the BBC, Radio Oranje. Our next broadcast will be at 8 a.m. tomorrow morning.

"Long live the Queen."

Chapter Two

A CHANGED MAN

The road to Utrecht was easy to travel on a bicycle. The meadows were still green, lush and inviting, because the flowering dandelions, buttercups and blue bonnets were still adorning the fields in a pallet of colors. The birds hiding in between the tall flowery grasses and field flowers were unaware of the pending hunger of winter.

It was fall 1944…

The number of grazing cattle was amazingly small. Sheep and goats were long gone, eaten by hungry Nazis. Cows, normally carrying calves around the fall time were skinny; even breeding had come to an end because of the lack of bulls. The crisp fall air felt good for the blonde traveler. His bicycle was clearly marked with a tag which said "Geestelijke" (clergy) and to accentuate the occupation of the rider he had painted several crosses on the bicycle. His Ausweiss (ID) was in the breast pocket of his jacket, sticking out partially, just in case a German soldier would want to see it.

The Ausweiss read *Dominee Henk de Groot, Hervormde Kerk Den Haag*. The three other Ausweisses were all hidden in his boots. One of them read *Rabbi Levi Strauss*; it had a big red J on it which meant Jewish. He was daily reminded not to carry that ID with him.

He had been advised to destroy it by his friends in the Resistance many a time. But his Jewish pride prevented him from getting rid of it. The third Ausweiss he carried read *Han de Clerck, Insurance salesman*. His picture with the blonde hair proved that is was him. That Ausweiss was his biggest bluffing device, because whenever he was caught with a family in their home, he used it to prove why he was visiting.

His fourth and last Ausweiss read *Cor van der Weiden*. He carried them all in different places in the lining of his boots. He knew that it was dangerous because if he was frisked and the Nazis found them, he stood a chance of getting shot on sight. This last ID was used when he was at a farm, visiting and encouraging his fellow Jews in their hiding places. He would even dress the part of a farm hand, but he would act as a simpleton.

Amazingly he had never been frisked, and that was because, nearly always, he was on the road when the German patrols would stop him. In those instances, which were sometimes as many as ten times a day, he would play the part of Dominee Henk de Groot. Sometimes he would take his Bible and begin reading it in front of the soldiers who, afraid of being convicted by his preaching, would let him go quickly. Who would ever think of frisking a reverend preacher anyway?

So far, Levi had been very successful with his disguises. He had been a blessing to the Jews all over the country who were in hiding and scared to death of being caught. He had been able to pray with them and perform several Jewish celebrations, such as Seder, Hanukkah and Rash-Hashanah.

While he was riding his bicycle to the city of Utrecht, once a proud and clean city in the center of the country, he was reflecting on his newly accepted faith. He had been praying, and was still praying, about how to present himself – the former Rabbi – now a Christian, to his fellow Jews in the hiding places. Would they still accept him as a spiritual leader? How was he going to present himself and talk about the Jesus they had always rejected? Vaguely a plan was forming in his mind. He would begin by asking why they believed Christians were hiding them. He would persuade them to tell him why those people in particular were doing so much for them at the risk of their own lives.

When he finally arrived at the farm on the outskirts of Utrecht, he realized that he hadn't been stopped the entire way from The Hague. Some 60 miles, and not one Nazi had he encountered. That was odd, to say the least. What was going on? Then a thought entered his mind, Was he supernaturally protected now that he had accepted Jesus as his Lord and Savior? *Was that the reason why all the Christians who were hiding Jews had been so successful and why so few had been found out?*

The realization gave him inspiration to face his fellow Jews at the farm he was about to visit. He rode the long driveway to the farmhouse; the farmer's wife had seen him coming and was ready when he dismounted his bicycle.

"Rabbi Strauss, so nice to see you. The people have been asking for you, something about Hanukkah or something," she greeted him.

The Rabbi held his finger to his lips in a gesture to be silent and walked over the threshing floor towards the upper room that every old farmhouse had. It was the room where guests were entertained most of the time, a room for special occasions. He sat down and looked at the farmer's wife with great sympathy. Here was another family of Christians risking their lives for the Jewish people.

"My dear, Dora", he began, "I am officially no longer a Rabbi," he announced, causing her eyes to open wide with surprise.

"What happened Rab...eh...? Levi? Or did you change your name as well?"

He shook his head and dramatically proclaimed, "I accepted Jesus as my Lord and Savior, just a few days ago, and I need help on how to behave about this in front of the Jews you have in hiding. I know you'll have a million questions and I have been praying about this all the way from The Hague. Please ask your husband to come here so we can discuss this together and pray about it before I face them."

Maarten, the farmer, walked into the upper room to find out why his wife was in there with someone, expecting a German to have intruded their farm. But when he saw who had arrived, his eyes lit up and with outstretched arms he came towards the visitor. "Rabbi Strauss, what a great surprise to see you here so unexpectedly."

"The surprise is all mine, Maarten," the visitor spoke while he put his arm over the wife's shoulder and his other arm over Maarten's. He said it again as he was going to have to say it many times in the coming days. "I accepted Jesus, because He is the only one in these difficult times who can give the strength to all those who are hiding Jews to accomplish what they are doing. Now I need help to continue my service to those in hiding. I can be a teacher and a comforter, a Dominee, if you will, but I can no longer be called a Rabbi and I am at a loss how to present that to them."

"This is wonderful, Levi, but you must take a different name too, so no one will make the mistake at calling you by your Jewish name," said Maarten. "What shall we call you from now on?"

They all laughed. The Joy of the occasion filled the room; and when the converted Jew opened his mouth the word came out unexpectedly without even thinking about it.

"Peter… I want to be called Peter, because Jesus said, 'Upon this Rock (talking to Peter) I will build my church.' I want to be used to bring the Good News to the Jews in hiding, all over this country. They will understand Who is really saving them from certain death. Thank you both; you have provided the answer to the questions I have been wrestling with today, all the way from The Hague to Utrecht."

Hungry children, on wooden shoes.
The schools were closed.

The three of them went to the hayloft in the back of the farm above the stables where, at one time, more than a hundred cows were kept. But now only six skinny cows were eating the remains of sugar beet pulp.

There simply was not enough food for the people, let alone for the animals. The Nazis had taken cow after cow until Maarten had strongly protested at the risk of being shot. The Sergeant had shaken his head but then he reassured Maarten that he understood that as a farmer he had to keep at least some live-stock to be able to continue his profession.

In the far corner of the stable was a stack of hay bales, stacked as high as possible. What no one could see was that the entire stack was on small rollers. In fact, eight rollers made of steel pipes had been welded together with pins which stuck deep into the hay. A set of heavy beams on the floor prevented the hay stack from moving. But when the beams were removed, one push to the left would roll it sideways revealing … nothing. What one could see behind it was a typical small stable where the calves were usually kept and nurtured. The ceiling was made of wood planks, nothing unusual.

Maarten picked up a shovel and with the end of it he knocked at the ceil-ing three times. It remained very quiet, not a sound could be heard. Maarten knocked again, this times only two knocks. At the same time he said with a calm voice, "Shalom Shabbat."

From above the ceiling came the reply, "Sjema Jisrael."

One by one the ceiling planks were removed and a ladder was lowered from the loft. When the three visitors went up the ladder enthusiastic greetings sounded and great joy was seen on the faces of the hidden when they recog-nized their visitors.

The hiding place had never been found by the Nazis because careful mea-sures had been taken to enter . In addition, the strictly kept rules were not to make any unnecessary noise, not to walk around, and to stay on the loft, which was quite big and ran across the entire stable. An intricate warning system which sounded as if a cow was lowing had been installed with the help of an old fashioned telephone.

When the Nazis paid a visit to the farm it was not unusual that they heard cows lowing. The stack of hay bales had been shot at several times. No soldier had ever attempted to move it and no sound had ever come out of the hay when it had been shot at.

The reception in the attic of the stable had been abundant and joyful; a full ten minutes of greeting and hugging the Rabbi. Finally, in the sight of the hid-den Jews the "Rabbi" raised his hands and requested all to be quiet.

"Sit down my friends. I have a lot to tell you and I know you like to hear news of what is going on in the outside world. But first I will need your full attention. I have a very important announcement to make."

The eighteen fugitives found a seat around Levi and sat down on the hay with which the entire attic was covered, because there were no chairs or tables. The floor was their only place of comfort and it was even used for their beds. They had become used to their lifestyle, and, if it were not for the total isolation from the world, the hiding place was not the worst place to be during the threatening wartimes.

It was very quiet and all eyes were aimed at the former Rabbi. Expectant eyes looked at the only one among them who was able to travel and visit them and many other friends of the same fate. When he finally spoke his voice sounded a little hoarse.

"My dear friends, what I am going to tell you is great news and I want you to listen with an open mind. Before I tell you what has happened to me, I need to ask you a question. Why do you think these people here, your graceful hosts, and all the other people in the country are doing what they are doing, risking their lives and working hard to hide you all? I will go around the circle here and I would like to hear a short answer from each of you."

He pointed at the person sitting closest to him and waited for the answer, "Because they love us Jews," the first person answered.

The next person was a young lady. Esther was her name and the first thing she said was, "I have been at four different hiding places and one thing they all had in common, they were all Christians. Does that have any significance?"

Levi merely nodded and looked expectantly at the next person who said, "I agree with Esther, but could that be the reason they are taking this huge risk? I think it is because they feel sorry for us."

The answers kept coming. Most of them were vague and all the answers came down to the same ideas that had been mentioned before. This went on until about the twelfth person, Hazel Klein began. The Rabbi felt it coming and could not wait to hear her say what he wanted to hear.

"Because they all believe that we, the Jews, are God's chosen people and they believe that Jeshua came to set us (and them) free. I am getting to a serious point in my thinking where I might believe them. I had been reading the Bible with the last family I stayed with and it all makes sense."

The young Hazel Klein looked around the circle and into the eyes of her friends and boldly proclaimed, "I have become a Christian because of them. Because they believe in Jesus they are protected from the wiles of the devilish Nazis. I know it and I strongly recommend all of you to think about it. Even you, Rabbi Strauss." The only reaction of the Rabbi was that he made a big smile.

Some of the Jews began to protest. All of them were surprised about the statement which had just been made and some of them began to plead with Hazel saying that she had made a wrong decision. The Rabbi raised his hand and urged everyone to be quiet.

"My dear, dear friends," he began, "most of your reasons stated here in the last fifteen minutes are correct and acceptable, but I have to agree that Hazel's answer is the best and, in my eyes, the only truth I have heard so far."

For a few minutes it became deadly quiet on the hayloft, but then…

Some of the older men began to protest against the Rabbi's statement, but he waved his hand and continued after two minutes of utter silence.

"I, too, have come to that conclusion. I, too, have become a Christian." Nothing broke the dead silence that followed his statement. If the floor had not been covered with hay you could have heard a pin drop.

After at least five minutes of utter silence, everyone with downcast eyes, it was Maarten, the famer, who broke the silence and began to speak.

"I must agree with your conclusions. I know that all the people who are hiding Jews and helping them to survive do it out of their Christian conviction that the Jewish people are God's chosen people and also because it says in the Bible, *'There is no greater love than a man who lays down his* life for another.' My wife and I believe that way and pray that all of you will be saved.

"Ladies and gentlemen, my dear guests and friends, may I introduce to you Dominee Henk de Groot."

There was no applause. The lack of it could have been for two different reasons; they did not agree with the Rabbi or they knew they should not make any noise in their hidden dwelling place. They all had a lot to consider and reconsider in the upcoming days.

Chapter Three

UNUSUAL TRAFFIC

Kees and Cornelius had been traveling on their bicycle for seven hours. They were both exhausted, hungry and able to eat a horse or raw beans, whichever came first. It was at this time that they were stopped by a German patrol, just before they entered the city of Wageningen.

The hated but unfortunately familiar, "Halt. Ausweiss," sounded harsher than ever. The soldiers looked through the bicycle bags and asked why there was nothing in them. They frisked Kees thoroughly and wondered why they could not find anything on him either. Then they looked at Cornelius. At the same time Kees gave him the sign and Cornelius began to bawl so loud that every soldier was looking in their direction. They looked almost accusingly at the two soldiers who had been frisking Kees. A sergeant joined the scene and said, "Wass ist loss mit ihm?" Kees shrugged his shoulders and answered in Dutch, "Altijd honger." (Always hungry.)

The Sergeant stroked Cornelius' hair and said, "Einem moment, bitte," and went to the temporary office that they made at the roadblock by kicking out the inhabitants of a home. After minutes he came back with a package and handed it to Cornelius and said, "Bitte und gehen zu Hause, schnell."

When they rode away on their bicycle, Cornelius began to laugh,"That was the first time I received something from the Moffies." When he opened the package he found two fried chicken legs, ready to eat. Kees could not resist the tears welling up in his eyes as he realized at that very moment, that even during this nasty war, the Lord would make his enemy give them food. The enemy was human after all. He decided to find a roadside bench and while eating the treasured food he would teach his son about God's ability to turn the enemy into friends.

It was getting darker when they resumed the trip. Kees realized that he had only half an hour before it would be completely dark and that curfew would begin a half hour after that. So in one hour he had to reach the farm in Rhenen or he would risk being arrested. He pushed his pedals a little harder. Once he reached the top of the hill he could relax and let the downside of the hill take him to the farm without having to push it.

Their destination was a hog farm, hidden in the pine woods at the edge of the Veluwe, the middle part of the country where endless rolling low hills displayed the splendor of the purple heather fields, separated by green pastures and pine trees. This area was often shunned by the Nazi troops because the Resistance could be anywhere. Many times an entire platoon had been attacked and ambushed with too many casualties. There was nothing to steal on the Veluwe except at the sparsely scattered farms; but they had been visited too many times to have any food left for the marauding soldiers.

The gate to enter the farm was locked and the only way to get in was by shaking the big cowbell that hung on the tall pole next to the gate. Kees knew that it could take fifteen minutes before the farmer would show up because he would first sound the alarm for the Jews hidden in the basement.

The place where twenty four Jews had found refuge and where some of them had lived for almost two years had been a former dung pit, built beneath the stables where, at one time before the war, as many as five hundred hogs had been living their noisy lifestyle. Every day the farmer would chase the pigs to the outside pen and hose out their droppings which would run into the huge basement. Once a month a tanker truck would suck out the contents and clean out the dung cellar.

It had been two years since Kees had visited the farmer and asked him if he would hide some Jewish guests for a short time. The guests would be on their way out of the country and needed a regular sleeping place. At first the farmer had refused saying that he did not have a place to hide any Jews. Kees had persuaded him by telling him how many people had disappeared from the Netherlands and that the Nazis were killing millions in the death camps in Germany and Poland.

After hours of discussion the wife of the farmer had come back from church. When she heard about Kees's plea, she told the two men what the preacher in church had mentioned that very evening. The Jews are God's chosen people and that we, as Gentiles, have an obligation to take care of them. God would bless those who would do so and protect them from any harm.

At that point in the discussion the farmer had only one argument left. "Where am I going to put them on this stinky farm?" Kees had proposed to look around the farm and see if he could make a suggestion. He had stumbled upon the dung cellar which had just been cleaned out that day.

"Do you need that cellar all the time?" had been his question. "Is there any way you can divert the dung somewhere else now that you have only forty pigs left?"

They had both laughed about the irony; a hog farm of all places, to hide Jews. Here they were suggesting hiding them at the very place they considered non kosher, even worse to hide them in a hog-dung cellar. After some time of discussion the plan had been adopted. The farmer had promised to clean the cellar further to make a separate entrance at an inconspicuous place and to change the run-off into the cellar in such a way that it still looked as if the dung went down.

He had reported, by sending his fourteen year old daughter to The Hague on her bicycle, a week later that the refuge place was ready to receive guests. It had become a great place for the Resistance. It was hardly ever visited by the Nazi patrols and, on the few occasions they had come, they had left with the opinion that there was no use searching that stinky hog farm. No Jew in the country would ever want to hide there.

The farmer finally came to the gate and, when he saw whom his visitors were, the worry on his face was replaced with joy.

"Kees and Cornelius! How are you? What brings you to this stinky place of mine and at this hour of all times? Your bell ringing startled me. You know I have not seen a visitor for weeks. Have you forgotten me here in this lonesome place?"

He kept on talking while he unlocked the padlock on the gate and opened it for the two visitors and their bicycle.

The three of them walked to the farmhouse where the worried look on the farmer's wife had also disappeared to make place for a big smile. *They were good people, the van Zantens,* Kees thought to himself as he walked into the house.

They hugged and exclaimed words of joy to see the two visitors; there was an atmosphere of happiness, which was rare in this awful war-torn country.

When the first greetings were passed, Mina van Zanten said, "Let me go and announce the great news of your arrival downstairs and put our guests at ease. Then we'll pour some surro for us and some chocolate milk for the boy and have some quality time to find out what brings you two here today."

She was back three minutes later and began to make the promised drinks, all the while talking about how hard it was to feed all the guests. She reflected on how, at first, they had refused to eat pork; but as they became hungrier they had finally given in. How difficult it was to get bread and even flour to bake it. She had grown a small field of potatoes and she was coming to the final supply of that.

"Do you have any suggestions as to what she could do to obtain some basic food like flour or just grain to make flour?"

Kees promised her he would see if some other farmers could supply what she needed. The problem was getting it to them. Kees asked the farmer,"Karel, do you have any suggestions on how we could get some sacks of grain to you, if I find it?"

"The only way I can think of is to bring it to the feed supply company and have them bring it to me in hog feed sacks." He gave Kees the address of the feed company and Kees promised to look into the situation as soon as he could.

"Remember we have only enough till the end of the week and twenty-four hungry guests will become very hungry indeed."

After some more conversation, Kees asked if they could stay for the night and asked to go see the guests in the cellar.

"I brought ID's for two people. Let's see, for Dr. Eli de Knecht and his secretary Magda. They are going to be picked up to go to Switzerland the day after tomorrow. The details of their pick-up and their way of transportation are in my head and I will give you those before I leave tomorrow. I guess Magda is his daughter, having the same name. Or is she his wife? I know one thing they are desperately needed in England for their expertise and knowledge. The bombardments of London are causing thousands of casualties even among doctors. Eli is supposed to be a bone specialist and they don't seem to have one there in London. So let's go and talk to all the people, and if you could be so kind as to bring the good doctor and his Magda upstairs, I will talk to them in private about their pending escape trip to Switzerland."

When they entered the cellar through the secret door that Karel had created when he had transformed the dung cellar into a hiding place, the guests all jumped up from their improvised tree trunk seats and welcomed Kees with great enthusiasm and expectation. Who was going to get transported this time was the big open question each of them had on their mind. What news are the tall Gentile and his tiny son bringing from The Hague? After greeting the visitors Kees gestured them to take a seat and pay attention to him.

"Shalom, my friends. I have some great news to share with you," Kees began. "The end of the war is getting closer. Now don't jump to any conclusions, yet. There are rumors that the Canadians are going to land soon and the Allieds have taken most of Belgium back. Presently they are fighting in Luxemburg, but being so mountainous and so close to Germany where supplies and fresh troops are coming from, that may take a while.

"The Nazis are getting nervous and some of them are getting overly friendly, as we experienced today. As soon as the Allies have made a breakthrough in the Ardennes in Luxemburg, we will be next. The Resistance is asking you to be patient for just a little while. Don't take any risk going outside. Just wait for the all clear sign from the government. Your host, Karel, has a hidden radio and he will be instructed when the time comes what to tell you and where to go. Until then, hang in there and enjoy your vacation." They all laughed about the word *vacation.* Kees thought, *if they only knew...*

"The next good news I have to bring you is that your Rabbi will be here soon. Rabbi Levi Strauss told me himself that he is coming by here in the next few days, and I can personally tell you that he will have some very exciting news for you."

When Kees turned around to go back upstairs, a barrage of questions were shot at him, but he shook his head and said, "No more questions please, I need some rest after a full day of riding my bike with my son, being hungry and under constant threat from the Nazis. Have a good night and I will see you tomorrow morning before I leave."

Karel had silently ushered the two candidates for departure upstairs while the others had been shooting questions at Kees. He had sat them down at the kitchen table and when Kees joined them they had their questions ready.

"What is going to happen with us, Kees? Are we being taken away from here soon? We need to know so we can be prepared now that the war is coming to an end."

Kees made a gesture with his hands which meant to take it easy and please listen.

"First of all the war is by no means ending yet. The end may be in sight but it might still take another year and for that reason the government in London, the Queen herself, has expressed the wish to get you to London as soon as possible. Because you are a knowledgeable doctor and one of a few in your specialty, we have received all the necessary tools to get you there quickly. I brought with me new ID's for you in the name of Cor and Annie de Slechte.

"Tomorrow morning at seven a.m. you need to be ready in the woods by the gate. Karel will bring you there and a German ambulance will pick you up. Don't be alarmed by the Nazi ambulance and the German-looking driver and helper. They are members of the Resistance; highly trained and fast. The ambulance will stop for a split second and when the door opens you must jump in quickly. The door will open only when all is clear. The driver will press the brake lights two times and that will be the all clear sign. You will have to be fast though. Do you understand so far?"

The two had listened intensely and nodded their heads in understanding. Eli had a question: "What if they see that we are both healthy once inside the ambulance when the Nazis stop us?"

"That is a good question, Eli, but we are accustomed to those situations. Let me explain. While the ambulance drives away, you will be 'installed' in the ambulance. You, Magda, will be laid down beneath the floor on which the stretcher sets. Eli, you will be dressed as a German Officer. Your head will be bandaged and you will become virtually unrecognizable. Don't worry, Magda, you will be comfortable in a soft bed underneath the stretcher."

"We have never had anyone arrested in transport on our ambulances; besides your ID's will match the paperwork which the driver carries. If the Nazis look inside the ambulance they will simply see a wounded German officer and they will have no reason to look any further."

The doctor and his wife, as Kees had just found out, were excited but still a little apprehensive.

"What if the liberation came on their way to Switzerland and what if they had a problem with the ambulance?"

Kees assured them once more. "We have never had a problem. The ambulances are serviced by mechanics all the time. They have extra large gas tanks and we even fill the gas tanks at the German gas stations without ever raising any suspicion."

Finally the two accepted the proposal and began to get enthusiastic about the prospect of being in a free country, even though it was being bombed every night.

"By the way," Kees continued, "Don't tell the others down stairs about your departure until you leave tomorrow morning. We don't want to create any unrest amongst you". Kees stood up and shook their hands saying: "May God be with you, Shalom."

He never saw them again.

Chapter Four

BACKYARD NURSERY

—※—

Johanna had an extra task to take care of when Kees was on the road with Cornelius. In fact, Cornelius had given her two tasks to do when he was gone. The first one was to check his garden. The city back yard was only forty by fifty feet in size and the boy in his fourth year of age had created a neat garden where he was growing all kinds of vegetables and flowers. The family, including the temporary guests beneath the house, all ate from the garden and fresh vegetables were a luxury during World War II. While most vegetable growers had been put to work at the German war industry, the brave ones who still grew vegetables were looted by the Nazis whenever the crop was ripe for harvest.

Around the fence of the garden, Cornelius had sown marigolds that were blooming abundantly with large orange flowers. Sometimes he would bring some of the flowers to an aunt who lived down the street and other times he would present his mother with a flowery bouquet. One time he brought a small bouquet to the two Jewish girls who lived down the street; but they were gone one day and he never saw them again.

Johanna had to check the garden for ripe plants or strawberries and to water them when needed; a job Cornelius took care of anytime he was at home.

The other task she had to do for him was a little more complicated. It was a task she had to delegate to one of Cornelius' friends because she could not climb on the roof of the Groenendijk Warehouse next door. The friend he had instructed to do the job had to be picked up every day and Johanna would help him climb on the roof to take care of the carefully maintained pigeon egg farm Cornelius had created. He had to mark one egg and take out the previously marked egg every day.

That morning when Cornelius left the hog farm in the woods near Rhenen he was thinking about his little farm at home. On the way back to the city he determined to ask Marie at the Brandwijk farm what, if anything, he could grow during the coming winter. Perhaps he could build another greenhouse. He would definitely go look for duck eggs again because he could keep those in the little pen during the winter and feed them little fish from the river nearby his home. What else could he grow that made food for the coming winter?

They were on their way to the city of Arnhem, a place where many Jews used to live. Now, in the fourth year of the war, it was a place where more Germans than Dutch were living. The Nazis had gradually commandeered the homes of the citizens, chasing them out and stealing all their furniture and possessions.

For six months a steady stream of homeless people had wandered across the countryside searching for a place to live. Now the winter was coming and fear gripped the people. Would there be food? Would there be more homeless people swarming the streets and the countryside?

The Jews were gone and sometimes a wandering family would stumble upon an abandoned Jewish home. When such a home was entered, it would be occupied in a matter of days with five, six or more families who finally had found a place to sleep out of the cold and the rain.

No home, no food and no father.

Sometimes they would stumble onto a child who had been left behind and who had not been noticed by the marauding Nazis. In those cases the child was immediately adopted into the family who had found her. No questions asked; this child was now a Dutch child. Whether Jewish or not, she was Dutch and a chosen child of God. Such was the mentality of the Dutch everywhere and in all situations.

Kees and Cornelius left that morning at five o'clock. They had a long ride through the fruitful lands of The Betuwe to a small town close to the suburbs of Arnhem. The early morning was crisp that fall. The blue sky was full of freedom's promises. It was as though the heavens declared that liberation was underway. The river Rijn was peaceful and the road along the river had no barricades; until nine in the morning it remained serene and still.

Suddenly, the sound of boat engines broke the peace and quiet of the landscape. A large sand barge came by pulled by a smoking tugboat. Something odd was going on with the barge. Behind it were three German patrol boats. On the bow of each of them were mounted machine guns and soldiers were aiming at the barge. Through a loudspeaker the Germans were demanding the tugboat to stop. Apparently the captain of the tugboat either did not hear the command or did not want to listen because it seemed as if the tugboat increased its speed as large plumes of smoke emerged from its big black chimney.

The pursuing soldiers began to shoot at the barge. A constant barrage of bullets was popping holes in the barge at its waterline. The battle looked like a passing parade in the streets at carnival time. But this was real and Kees and Cornelius were watching the fight first hand.

The sound of cries could be heard from the inside of the barge and as the volume of the cries increased so did the shooting. Within minutes two of the patrol boats hooked onto the barge while the third one went on towards the tugboat. Dozens of soldiers, arms ready, walked on the gangways and disappeared into the barge. Shots could be heard inside the barge, then loud screams, then silence…

The third patrol boat had hooked onto the tugboat and the captain emerged from the cabin with his hands in the air. The three soldiers who jumped towards the captain fired their guns at the captain. Father and son could see the complete shock on his face. Then he fell and tumbled into the icy water of the Rijn.

Kees and Cornelius had watched the entire battle from the beginning to the end. They were hidden between the tall bulrushes on the side of the river. Apparently the soldiers had turned off the engine of the tugboat. As suddenly as the quiet had been broken by the short battle it returned as if nothing had happened. Even the soldiers made no sound. Kees could see them perusing the countryside on both sides of the river and it seemed as if they were looking for possible spectators. Kees shivered and pushed Cornelius deeper down into the bulrushes. He held his finger to his lips and whispered to him, "Don't move, son!" They remained very still for what seemed a whole hour.

Finally they heard some commands and the engines of the patrol boats were started. The three Nazi vessels all went to the far side of the barge and pushed it towards the secret watchers until it landed against the side of the river into the very bulrushes which had protected the two from view. A rush of water came right up to their hiding place. Kees hoped it would not flush them out but then he realized they could not be seen anymore because the high side of the barge was between them and the watching eyes of the Nazis.

Kees realized they had witnessed a war crime and he made the decision to investigate the barge as soon as the patrol boats had left. Finally, the peace and quiet and the beauty of a calm river, edged with fall colors, had returned and the birds began to sing again. Kees stood up. Cornelius followed his dad in the direction of the stranded barge. Carefully he looked from side to side and across the river to see if anyone was approaching the scene of the crime. There were no farms nearby. The closest church tower could be seen at the sky line. But that was too far for anyone to have heard the shots.

Still, Kees remained cautious as he stealthily moved towards the barge. He had to wade through the water in between the bulrushes and gestured to Cornelius to stay on the wall between the high reeds. He saw a rope hanging from the rusty side of the vessel and tugged on it to see if it would hold his weight. Then he began to climb. It was a tough job to pull himself up about twenty feet and when he reached the top he was glad he could hold onto the solid steel railing. With a swing of his legs he pulled himself onto the deck. He did not want to stand tall and expose himself so he crawled along the gangway until he could look over the steel edge into the hold. What he saw was enough to make him scream. He held himself and his emotions in check just in time. There must have been some fifteen bodies strewn on top of a pile of sand down at the bottom of the barge.

After five minutes of shock he regained his composure and studied the situation to figure out his way down into the barge. On the opposite side was a stairway; it must have been the one the soldiers had used to get down into the hold to do their dirty work. Kees crawled around the hold towards the stairway. Quickly he slipped over the edge of the steel hold of the ship and went down the stairway.

His first action was to check if there were any survivors. One by one he checked the pulse of each body. The blood had colored the sand and he carefully tried to avoid stepping into the red blotches. No one had survived. He looked around in the huge hold of the barge to see if there were any others, but the giant room could not hide anyone.

The ship began to take on water through the bullet holes the soldiers had created. Kees decided that the vessel could not sink much further since it was stranded on the shallow side of the river. He went back to the bodies he had examined before and began to check for identifications, but he found none. Then he checked for purses and wallets, but there were none. Then he noticed one of the left arms had a number tattooed onto it. When he looked at the other bodies he noticed they all they all had numbers tattooed on their arms. He finally realized that what he had witnessed was the murder of fifteen Jews.

How and why they were ever on board the barge, no one will ever know. Perhaps they had been put there by the Nazis or they had escaped from a concentration camp. The one thing Kees had to do was to get them buried and for that he would need the help of the local Resistance. He would have to go back to Rhenen and ask Arie to find the local leaders of the Resistance. They would have to take it from there.

Kees sighed, "Is there no justice for such a crime?" No, there was none because the killers had shot 'fugitives' and in their eyes they were outlaws!

Kees had done his ugly duty after he visited the hog farm again and Arie had directed him to the local Resistance leaders. His mind was in great turmoil over the incident. He wanted to find out who these criminals were and to keep their names until after the war. But any action he would undertake could expose him and he had too many people to take care of. He had told the ringleader in Rhenen that three patrol boats had been involved in the incident, but he did not have any boat numbers or description of the soldiers. They would get away with it. Only God could convict them…

They were under way again; destination Oosterbeek, close to the big city of Arnhem. He hoped to deliver his distribution cards quickly and ride back the next day, back to the Brandwijk farm and The Hague where he could cry together with his beloved Johanna. Little did he know what he would find first.

Chapter Five

JEWS WITHOUT THE STAR

It was way too late to reach Oosterbeek that day, so Kees decided to go to a farm about twenty kilometers south of Arnhem. He had only been there once and he planned to be careful in approaching the place. In these war years one had to be very careful. The Nazis would take possession of any house or farm and kept a constant surveillance on certain locations. Krelis van Houten had a farm with some milk cows and he grew hay for the winters and some sugar beets to sell to the city people.

Far in the fields, he had a small orchard in the middle of which he used to grow potatoes. After the harvest he would hide his stash right there in the ground. He had done that for the first four years of the war and the Nazis had never found anything worth stealing from him, except some cows. The first time they came they had taken two cows from his small herd of nine. The second time they came he had told them they could not take any more cows or he would be out of business and unable to supply the Nazis with milk and cheese which he made right there on his little farm.

The commandant of the garrison had been a farmer himself and as such he understood this rough Dutch farmer. He had agreed to that as long as Krelis would supply them with twenty liters of milk a day and a big round wheel of cheese every month.

A day after the compromise a young man came to his farm. He seemed like a nice young man but he looked very hungry. The young man introduced himself as Geert Jansen and asked for a job. He told Krelis that he was an Agricultural student and that he had been trying to avoid being picked up by the Nazis for the *Arbeits Einsatz.*

Krelis had his doubts about the young man, but getting cheap labor was a great benefit during the war considering most strong men had been taken into slave labor by the Nazis. The young man showed the farmer his ID which read *Geert Jansen.*

"Okay, I will try you out for a week and you better work hard or I will have to let you go." Krelis decided. He gave him a pitchfork and showed him what to do by turning the hay on the field. A few hours later the farmer's wife came and brought some coffee and bread. It was hard work, the day seemed very long and his hands began to blister, but he survived that first day. At six o'clock in the evening the farmer had put down his pitchfork and told him that they were quitting.

Half an hour later Krelis spoke.

"I will give you five guilders per week with food and lodging in the stable. You can stay because I am impressed with how you worked today being a city slicker." They shook hands and thus a long-term relationship had started for a Jew without a star. Krelis was not aware of having hired a Jew. He would never even have dreamed of hiring a Jew.

Every day Geert had to deliver milk to the German Garrison. The Nazis at the gate never guessed that a Jew was delivering their milk. A farm hand that walked in wooden shoes and worked on a farm was never a suspect for the Nazis.

The farmland that Krelis leased was on an estate owned by a Baron, who had become a voluntary member of the Waffen SS and had served at the Russian frontlines. Having been wounded, he had returned to Holland and after his recovery he had become a member of the notorious Sicherheits Polizei in The Hague. Baron van Boetselaer had become more than a traitor and worse than an NSB-er.

It was to that farm that Kees was heading. The farmer had a sister in The Hague for whom Kees had previously brought a message to Krelis and Kees had brought food back with him for the sister. Kees was hoping the farmer would still be there and that he would remember him from the year before.

Kees wondered if he was hiding anybody or if his farm had been compromised. If not, perhaps he could persuade the farmer to take some Jews for a while. He would be supplied with free, albeit fake, food stamps and have the protection of the Resistance.

It was getting close to dark and to curfew when he reached the beautiful Estate of Baron van Boetselaer and the farm of Krelis and his big family. Kees and Cornelius rode right up to the farm house; a yellow brick building built in 1652 as the dedication stone proudly announced. A young man was cleaning the yard and when he looked up both were greatly surprised. For a moment neither man knew what to say and, before Kees could say anything, the young man put his finger to his lips, the sign to say nothing until further notice.

At that time the farmer Krelis came to see who had arrived at this hour, just before curfew, and recognizing Kees, greeted him enthusiastically.

"Kees from The Hague isn't it? How are you? Are you bringing news from my sister?"

Kees shook his head. "No, Krelis, not this time. We just ran out of time to get to our destination and I wondered if you could put us up for the night. I did speak to your sister a week ago and she is doing well working in the hospital; you can imagine how busy that is at this time. She seemed to be happy; as far as one can be happy at such a time as this."

Krelis said he did not mind if they cared to sleep on the hay in the barn where the worker also stays. "Come inside so we can talk a bit about the war and the pending liberation," he suggested. "The wife might even brew up some surro and make you something to eat. We are always happy to see a visitor from the West."

They went inside. The farmhand stayed outside, continuing his job when Kees asked, "Where did you get your worker Krelis? Isn't it hard to get help in these days when the Germans pick up any men who can work?"

"Yes, but I got lucky. This guy is an agricultural student and they are exempt from forced labor as long as they work on a farm," Krelis replied.

"What's his name?" Kees asked, expecting it would not be the man's real name.

"He calls himself Geert Jansen, but I am not so sure that is his real name. He showed me his ID, but that does not mean a thing in these days. He is a good helper though. He works hard and sticks to himself. That is all that I care about."

Kees was relieved in a way and continued the conversation, choosing his words carefully. "Have you ever thought of hiding people here on this farm Krelis? As you know, there are thousands of people looking for hiding places since we know what the Nazis are up to in their concentration camps."

The answer did not surprise Kees, and yet it came as a slap in his face. "I don't want to have anything to do with Jews. I never asked for their help so they better leave me alone. I know that a lot of Christians keep them and that is their business. Not me. I stick to myself and don't go to any of those religious places. All they want is your money."

Kees left it at that. So many non-Christians had this attitude so it was no use fighting with them. He wondered how his friend outside had become involved with the farmer. He was soon going to get the answer.

Meanwhile, Betsy, the farmer's wife, had brewed some surro and brought in a plate of bread, sliced by hand, with delicious real butter and cheese. Cornelius looked at the slices and licked his lips. Betsy had brought him a steaming cup of milk. Cornelius thought he had come to heaven. While the men chatted, Betsy came to sit next to Cornelius and began to ask him all kinds of questions about what they were doing, their riding around the country and where they had been visiting. Cornelius knew he was never to give the correct answer; always say something else as his dad had commanded a long time ago.

Farmers go to bed early in the evening so Kees thanked the two hosts and father and son went to the old stable, where once fifty cows spent their winters. All stables in the farmlands of Holland had a loft which spread over the entire stable. It was the place where hay was stored. Above the troughs were hatches where the hay could drop down so the farmer did not have to haul hay from one end to the other.

The farmhand had made for himself a large pit in the hay so he could stay warm and cozy. It was there that Kees and Cornelius found him. He came towards the two visitors and embraced Kees firmly. He stroked Cornelius' hair and spoke very softly, "Kees, of all people, what are you doing here? Krelis is against Jews and he certainly is not hiding any as far as I know," he said with a smile.

"He does not know I am one because I am using the fake ID you supplied me with in The Hague."

"The house you sent me to in Arnhem got bombed. Most of the people died, including the hosts. I happened to be in the shack way in the backyard when it happened so I survived the bombing.

"I escaped Arnhem and became homeless, roaming through the forest for months. Finally I went back to Arnhem and was lodging with a prostitute. It was weird and scary because every day she had the Nazi customers come up to her room while I was in the next room. Finally I had enough of the tension not wanting to be discovered at a whore house and left. Again I roamed the woods until one day I stumbled upon this farm. It took a little persuading to be hired as a farmhand, my hands being so white and callous-less, but I worked really hard. So Krelis hired me for a token wage, food and lodging. I am safe here because the Nazis get milk and cheese from Krelis daily. I am the one who delivers it to the garrison," Geert told him with a big smile. "They know me over there now and have no suspicion that I am a Jew. I plan to survive the war without the yellow star."

Kees and Arie talked for a long time. Cornelius had been asleep for hours when Kees shook hands with Arie and wished him good night. When Kees and Cornelius left the next morning, both Arie and Krelis were already at work, far away in the fields.

Their final destination was Oosterbeek, a small town on the edge of Arnhem. Once there, Kees headed to a former fire station. The building had been partly bombed; two fire trucks could be seen beneath the rubble of stone and wood. The fire trucks were smashed and would never be used again. The Nazis searched the remains of the building once and decided it was not a place where anyone would ever want to hide. Little did they know that the inside of the fire trucks would give great safe living space to two Jewish families.

The Resistance had found the place and created a hidden entrance from the back alley. There was no light or water and washing had to be kept to a minimum. Once a week two Resistance members would each pick up a family and take them to their house for a shower and a warm meal. That's how these nine people survived thus far. Any place could be made useful as long as the Nazis shunned it.

Kees had to approach the bombed building from the back. He knew exactly what to do whenever he arrived there. There was a beam that hung just inside the opening through which he entered. At one time the opening had been a window. It had been narrowed down to a split of two feet wide and one could only slide inside moving sideways. The beam was stuck and hung slanted down from the ceiling onto the former windowsill. It was heavy and solid and, when someone in the know would arrive, the beam was used as a doorbell. Two knocks on the beam would sound throughout the building. Ten counts later one knock would alert the inhabitants that someone familiar was outside. Kees lifted Cornelius on his shoulders and let him make the first two knocks. Cornelius also did the ten- count and slammed the stick at the beam one more time.

They heard the handle of a truck door move and through the rubble, about twenty feet away, people began to emerge and come towards the two visitors. They knew the two and embraces followed. Everything was done in total silence. Some moved their mouths, silently articulating greetings. It took all of a minute and the building seemed to be back in its useless rubble status. All had gone back into the fire truck including Kees and Cornelius. There they still would talk in a quiet manner, but with great enthusiasm, because whenever Kees and Cornelius came there was news. News could be brought about the outside world or of a pending transport.

Dominee Henk de Groot, the former Rabbi had had his first encounter with his Jewish flock. It had been different in that most of them could not believe how a Rabbi could convert to Christendom. Some of them had shaken their heads but there had been quite a few who had been open to his change. His little questioning had made them think about all their former hosts and they had realized they all had one thing in common – they had all been Christians and they had all expressed that the Jews were God's chosen people. Out of the two visits the Rabbi made he had found that as many as five had also become Christians.

This time he was on his way to the hog farm of Karel van Zanten. He smiled when he thought about the irony of having Jews hidden at a hog farm.

The young Rabbi, now Dominee Henk de Groot, enjoyed riding his bicycle along the river Rijn. Little did he know that Kees and Cornelius had just traveled the same pathway, just three days before.

The weather was beautiful that early fall day in 1944. Though it had just turned into September, fall was in the air and he loved it. In the distance he saw a group of people doing something on the side of the river. A barge was nestled in the reeds and he saw people climbing in and out of the barge. He looked a little closer and noticed that there were no German soldiers at this activity so he decided to see what was going on. As he rode closer on his bicycle he noticed that there were two horse-drawn farmer's carriages on the roadside blocking the way and men were all loading something onto the carriages. Then he saw what they were loading; human bodies! When he stopped he saw a number of bodies already on the bed of the carriages and more were being brought from the barge.

His decorated bicycle with the crosses and fish painted on it gave him away. One of the men, still exhausted from carrying a body over his shoulder walked close by him. Henk reached his hand out to the man and introduced himself.

"Dominee de Groot," he said, meanwhile watching the man's reaction.

The man immediately called the others and pronounced, "Look guys, the Lord has sent us a clergyman to help us." The men all gathered around the two who had just shaken hands.

"What is going on here Gentlemen?" Henk inquired. One of them took charge of the answer after first introducing himself as Doctor Koomen.

"We had a messenger from the Resistance come to our house in Rhenen who told us that there had been an attack on this barge here and that there were fifteen bodies inside.

"We came to pick them up to bury them at our local cemetery. We tried to identify any one of them, but we could not find a clue. The only thing we found that was rather strange." He walked towards the closest carriage, "It was this..." he pointed at the tattooed forearms. "They all seem to have a number."

The Rabbi recognized the tattoos immediately and began to explain as he looked at some of the distorted faces, trying to recognize any of the Jews that had been piled on top of each other on the carriage.

"Gentlemen, I have to explain to you that I know what we have here. The people you have recovered are all Jewish. They must have escaped from one of the concentration camps and tried to get to a hiding place somewhere around here.

The Nazis must have found out about them and hunted them down. This is horrible; a crime against the human race, against the Jewish race. Oh. God. forgive them." The Rabbi's eyes filled with tears as he was looking at his people, killed and slaughtered like animals. He could not bear it any longer. He sat down in the grass and cried his heart out.

Chapter Six

CORNELIUS THE LITTLE FARMER

It is a long ride from Oosterbeek to The Hague, so Kees and Cornelius left at the crack of dawn. Kees had decided he would go through the Betuwe and see if he could find some food to take home. Knowing they would stop by the Brandwijk farm, he would try to bring them something from the fruited lands of the Betuwe where apples and pears grew in abundance. It also helped that the Nazis did not have time or the guts to go there, because the farmers who could be hiding in between the fruit trees had been known to act as snipers.

The endless orchards with fruit trees gave Kees the feeling that there could be peace again; that life went on. The Bible promised that seedtime and harvest would never cease. The beautiful countryside with streams running through it reminded him of Psalm One, *Like a tree planted by streams of water which brings forth fruit in its season.* "The war will end soon," he kept saying over and over.

The Americans are coming!

They stopped at an orchard which had a sign: FRUIT FOR SALE OR BARTER and rode the long driveway to the storage barn. They were not the only ones who had stopped. The price was not bad, considering it was war time. Kees loaded his side bags full with beautiful apples and pears; enough to share at the Brandwijk farm and give each guest a fruit of their choice. When he mounted his bicycle he could feel the weight of twenty five kilos of fruit. Cornelius had been given a large red apple to eat under way. It was still early in the morning when Kees pushed his pedals for the one hundred kilometer trip to Leidschendam and the Brandwijk farm.

The heavily loaded bicycle was noticed by the Nazis at the roadblocks and they all wanted to see what was in his bags and only two of them grabbed an apple. There was something in the air that made the Nazi soldiers seem milder and friendlier that day. Kees felt it, but could not pinpoint the reason. Was it the news of a pending invasion?

It took them ten hours to ride up to the Brandwijk farm. The entire family stood outside as usual. Kees missed their son, Cor, who had fallen while fighting for the freedom that was now on its way to the Netherlands. This family, so friendly and compassionate, welcomed the two exhausted travelers and ushered them into the upper room.

Kees said, "Hold on, Marie. Do you have a bowl or a basket? This time I brought something for you and your guests." He began to take out the delicious looking fruit one by one. The bags kept supplying apples and pears until he had counted twenty eight of them. "The rest is for us at home and I have twelve guests right now. How are you all doing? Did you have a good fall harvest this year?"

They chatted away for half an hour when Kees said, "Let's bring the fruit up to your guests here. I am anxious to see them." He called Cornelius who was nowhere to be found and Marie was gone too.

"Oh," said Kees, "he wants to know what he can grow in the coming months of winter and he wants to find duck eggs if he can."

The two friends of eighteen and four years of age were in the garden where Marie was showing Cornelius what he could plant at this time of the year. "I have a surprise for you, Cornelius. I know you will love it. Come on, let's go to the pig sty so I can show you." There in the pig sty was a double cage and inside were half a dozen rabbits.

Marie opened the cage and searched for a particular white rabbit. When she caught it by the fur of its neck it struggled at first and then it hung still.

"This, Cornelius, is a Vlaamse Reus. It grows very fast. It is not a pet to play with. Do you understand? This is food for our body after it is grown big. But there is one very special thing about this rabbit." She waited to make the announcement more dramatic. "This rabbit will be a mamma pretty soon. Do you think you can make room for twelve baby rabbits?"

Cornelius could not believe his ears. A mamma rabbit with twelve babies? He laughed aloud, "This is the best present I have ever had. I want to tell my father right now." He ran outside and towards the farmhouse but no one as there. Marie had followed him and she was smiling. It was so great to make the little guy happy every time he came.

"They must be in the haystack visiting your friends," she told him. They walked together, hand in hand, the two friends and then Marie watched him climb the ladder to the top of the haystack and disappear.

An hour later, they had only one hour left to get home before curfew. So they said goodbyes to the friends in the basement under the haystack, hugs were exchanged with the Brandwijks and Marie had put the big white rabbit in a gunny sack.

"Hold it on your lap like this and, if the Nazis stop you, tell them it is your pet and do your crying act. Have a safe little trip you two."

Amazingly they had not been stopped. It seemed as though all the road-blocks had been removed. Something was in the air and they could feel it.

Chapter Seven

FRENZY TUESDAY

In September 1944 it happened! Rumors had spread that the Canadians had landed near Arnhem and that the war was over. Suddenly the streets were full of people. Dutch flags were raised and everyone was singing and dancing in the streets.

The Nazi soldiers were nowhere to be seen as more and more speculation was being made of what was happening. NSB- ers were hauled out of their houses and literally stoned.

Suddenly there was gunfire in the Deiman Straat. A truckload of soldiers had arrived and were banging on the doors of the Groenendijk warehouse. The locks were shot open and a swarm of soldiers entered the warehouse. Moments later the soldiers came back out each riding a box-bicycle. A long line of soldiers was removing all the vehicles from Groenendijk's warehouse.

Mr.Groenendijk was helpless against all the guns and stood watching in shock at the exodus of his property. What was happening? Where were they taking them? He decided to follow them and see for himself. Normally the soldiers came and asked for his box-bicycles. They had always paid for them, but this time they had come with violence and taken his property by force. When he caught up with them he would demand returns of his property from the officer in charge.

The crowds returned to the streets after the incident. Kees and Johanna had watched the scene from behind their windows. Were the Nazis going crazy?

The people in the streets began to sing the national anthem and everyone was wearing something orange. Cornelius saw the color orange and thought of his long hedge of marigolds in the back yard. Quickly he went outside and picked a handful of them .

This was his opportunity! He ran into the streets and people who saw him with his big orange flowers began to ask him for them. They gave him money for each flower. Within minutes they were gone and in his hands he had all kinds of money. He went back to his back yard and returned to the streets over and over again. This was fun and it was madness; and he liked all the money he left on the kitchen table every time.

It took him an hour to sell each and every flower he had grown. *Tomorrow I need to go to the Brandwijk farm and get more flowers,* he thought, *and they have lots and lots of them!*

After the first hours of frenzy in the streets the festivities died down. The people went inside to celebrate. Kees wondered if it was it supposed to be that way? He went down below to see if he could pick up any news on the clandestine radio he had hidden there. Radio England, the BBC, reported that thousands of parachutists had landed near Arnhem. The fighting was fierce but that they had no doubt that a victory was imminent.

A different kind of frenzy was beginning to fill the streets of The Hague. The soldiers and the NSB-ers began to loot the stores and even the homes of people. Shots could be heard everywhere. When citizens protested against the looting, soldiers would shoot to shut them up.

A Thousands of vehicles, the most ridiculous contraptions, were filled with furniture, pets, paintings, pianos and beds; any kinds of household goods were stolen by the soldiers. A huge caravan of vehicles began to fill the streets on their way to the Heimat, the homeland of the Germans. The Dutch traitors followed their masters (stealing equally hard) to quickly get out of their own country, in fear of repercussions.

As the Nazis were leaving the city, chaos ensued in the entire West of the country. The distribution system for food began to fail. Food was being sold to any one, without the distribution stamps. The stores were empty within hours after they had received fresh supplies. The food stamps were no longer accepted and the prices went sky high due to the demand and a lot of greedy merchants.

Kees and Johanna were at a loss as to what they should do. Should they open up the hiding place and let the Jewish people go? Or should they wait and risk the death of their protégées, being unable to feed them?

The couple talked for a long time and they prayed for an equally long time; but no clear answer came. Was there a reason for the silence; for the consequences of the unknown? Kees decided to go to his friend, Frans, and discuss their situation along with a few more friends from the Resistance. The chaos made them more careful even though many neighbors lived it up; acting as if the war was already over.

When he arrived at Frans' house there were three other Resistance members meeting for the same reasons. They were all seeking advice from each other, yet no one had the answer. After hours of weighing the possible options, they decided that one of them should go to Arnhem and get first hand information on the progress of the Canadians. If the messenger could get through the lines to the Allied troops and talk to a General to see how their timing looked for a total surrender of the enemy then, and only then, could they begin to release their visitors. Officially the German command was still present in The Hague and, who knew, the Nazis could send fresh troops to regain order. They could still lose many of the fifty thousand Jews in hiding across the country.

Before the group broke up they had to appoint a volunteer to go to Arnhem. No one really felt called, but someone had to go. After ten minutes of discussions they decided it was Kees who should go. He was the one who knew the way and who had a lot of contacts in and around Arnhem. Even though he had just come from there, the need to get someone trustworthy at the war zone and check its progress was of greater importance.

Kees had an idea and brought it up as it came into his head. "I should get an ambulance from Ypenburg to take me. It will get me there quickly and safely and I can also get back through the chaos of the retreating Germans and NSB-ers."

Frans took the initiative to go to the airport hangar and arrange for the ambulance. They would have to pick Kees up early the next morning and in just over two hours they could be in Arnhem.

The trip to the battlegrounds was chaotic. The ambulance had been using its siren to get through the traffic. Hundreds and hundreds of contraptions had been put together to haul the stolen goods to the German border. The road was littered with broken down vehicles. Farmers' carriages were pulled, three at a time, with an old army vehicle which seemed to be on its last leg, puffing black smoke all over the roads.

This was a giant exodus of guilty people. The soldiers were not looking at the crowds who were yelling at them with an occassional obscene remark. The people were mocking the 'heroes' and laughing at them. No soldier dared to raise his gun. The NSB-ers were in the midst of the soldiers expecting them to protect them, but if there had been strong Dutchmen among the crowd they would have pulled them off their escape vehicles.

Alas, all the strong Dutchmen were still working for the Nazis somewhere east of there. Behind the lines, behind the war front the Canadians were fighting the Nazis who still had power to contain the slave laborers. They were never informed about the pending liberation. The Nazi slave drivers had seemed to become meaner as the end approached.

When the ambulance finally arrived in Oosterbeek, it had taken four hours instead of the normal two. This was as far as the driver dared to go. Shooting could be heard close by and occasionally a grenade exploded on the side of the street. This was the war zone!

Kees planned to go further on foot to get deeper into the battle zone; first and foremost to observe where the Nazis were and to find out how he could get to the Canadians. He needed local help and somewhere down the street he knew of a house where the Resistance used to meet. Would they still be there and, if so, would they know where to go?

Kees went to the back alleys of the town. Those alleys bordered on the fields and orchards that surrounded the one-street town. He noticed people behind the windows gesturing him to stay low.

It was a timely warning. Immediately he ducked. A split second later, a stray bullet hissed by him and shattered the window of the house behind him. Were they fighting this close? An older man came to the door and opened it just enough to show his face and called, "Sir, what are you doing here? This is the war zone! We had to stay in the basement all night because the bullets were hitting our house. Would you like to come inside and take shelter?"

Kees accepted the invitation. Perhaps the man knew where the action was and maybe he could tell him where to find the Canadians. As Kees came through the slightly opened door he noticed that the house was filled with people. He estimated there were at least fifteen.

There were no introductions from the scared people. He could see desperation in the eyes of most of them. One of them said, "Sir, sit down here behind this wall and rest a bit before you go back into hell again." The young lady who said this looked like she had not slept all night. Despite the urgency of his mission, Kees took the time to talk to these scared people. Was this their house? It looked to be in total shambles.

The old man began to explain, "I am the only one who normally lives here while the others are my neighbors. One family barely escaped a bomb that hit their house across the street. They happened to be just down the street when it happened. This house is not safe either, but at least we have a basement where we all tried to sleep. We attempted to but the fight went on around us all night. The Nazis have a hold on this town and the Canadians are on the other side of the river trying to come across."

Kees asked the man, "Is there any place I can get across to the Canadians?"

The man shook his head. "Not here, perhaps ten miles back, but I don't know for sure. There is a Ferry on the Rijn this side of the city Tiel. If it still runs, you might try there. If you were to cross here, both the Canadians and the Nazis will shoot at you."

After taking an hour of rest, Kees decided to find the ambulance and get a ride to the ferry. The ambulance had been parked in an abandoned warehouse where Kees found the driver asleep. He woke up with a shock, not expecting Kees back for hours.

"We need to go ten miles back to the Rijn, because the Canadians are on the other side of the river and there is no way we can cross it here without being shot at."

It was an odd scene to see the ambulance traveling against the oncoming traffic. The people on the side of the road raised their fists at the driver. The Nazis wondered what the ambulance was up to going in the wrong direction.

When it came to the turnoff towards the ferry the traffic eased up, but there were soldiers at the ramp. The Canadian soldiers surrounded the ambulance quickly and pointed their guns at the driver and Kees. They commanded them to get out of the ambulance and keep their hands up in the air. Kees and the driver were thoroughly checked for weapons and asked for their ID's. Of course they would have first produced their fake German Ausweiss; but this was different.

Kees, who spoke English fluently, asked for their commander. The sergeant in charge told him that he was the highest rank personnel present at this location. So Kees decided to explain to him what his mission was and why they were driving a German ambulance.

Even though it sounded acceptable, the sergeant told him that they would have to cross the river and be taken to their intelligence unit to be checked out. The ambulance had to be locked up and remain where it was.

Kees thanked the sergeant profusely. This is exactly what he desired and it was handed to him without having to take the risk of being shot at from both armies. Two armed guards boarded the ferry that quickly crossed the river. On the other side many soldiers were waiting to bring possible enemies to a large tent which housed the Canadian Intelligence.

The leader of the interrogators put the two men at rest and told them, "If you are who you claim to be, you have nothing to fear. You'll understand that you have entered the war zone and that everyone has to be checked out. By the same token, you could be German spies who came to have a look at our forces here."

It took more than an hour. Field phones had been used to verify the names and addresses Kees had given the intelligence officer. When he came back the man was very apologetic and friendly.

"Mr. van Rijn, you are who you said you are and you are welcome to go wherever you want to. I understand that you came to find out about the progress our troops are making. If you want to talk to one of our commanders I can arrange transportation for you. We will have to give you our uniforms to wear because you can imagine how it would look if you keep your Nazi uniforms on. We will supply you with what you need in a minute. I have made the arrangements for you already. You should not cross the river back to the other side in your Canadian outfits for obvious reasons. You are welcome to change into your Nazi uniforms when you have come back."

The delay, and the questioning had cost them more than five hours and the daylight was fading quickly. They would have to hurry to reach someone to stay with overnight and continue this quest the next day.

But where could they go? In his mind he searched for addresses on the south side of the River. Arnhem? What was south of Arnhem? He could not go east or he would run into the frontline and the ongoing battle. He would have to get away from the battleground and avoid the risk of getting injured. He also had to think of the ambulance driver who was with him.

"What do you think we should do for the night, Robert?" Kees asked. "Do you know anybody around here?" The driver shook his head. He had always slept in the ambulance after he found an abandoned building to park it in. He could hardly ask the Canadian soldiers. They were foreigners here and they would not know either.

Kees thought of the ferry captain. Now that they were no longer dressed in Nazi uniforms it would be much easier to get help. The ferry had just landed and when Kees stepped up to the captain, the man looked at the two with great surprise. "You two were German soldiers a few hours ago and now you are Canadians?"

Kees laughed and said, "Yes, we surrendered and they enlisted us at the same time. But sir, on a more serious note, I wonder if you can help us?" Kees avoided giving any information about themselves. One could never be too careful. "We need a place to sleep for the night. Do you know of someone loyal to the Hollanders or even a hotel which is still in business?"

The man thought for a moment and then said, "There is a farmhouse just south of here. It used to provide bed and breakfast and I believe they are still there. It is only two kilometers if you follow the river. It's the only farmhouse you will see below the dyke. They used to have a sign and that might still be there too. The only thing is that they never took in soldiers. The Nazis tried to stay there but they would not give in. I am surprised they survived the Nazi pressure. I think it will be your best bet. Gentlemen, I've got to cross the river again. My boat is full. Good luck".

Kees and Robert took off, briskly walking the two kilometers along the river. They could see the farmhouse after walking less than half an hour. It was almost dark when they stood in front of the entrance gate to the farm. A big black Bouvier dog was barking at them and from the farmhouse the silhouette of a man emerged and began strolling towards the gate. He commanded the dog to be quiet and called from twenty meters away, "We don't take soldiers here, gentlemen."

Kees called, "Sir, please hear us out for a minute. We are dressed like soldiers, but that is because we are in the Resistance." And then he said the password, "Graag." When the farmer heard 'the word', pronounced the way only the Dutch could, he came closer and took a good look at them.

In broken English he said, "You no Canadians?"

Kees replied, "We are as Dutch as one can be, sir. Please put us up for the night and we will tell you all about our mission."

The farmer nodded, "Goed kom maar binnen," (Ok, come on inside) and opened the gate. The big black dog was watching at a distance. Kees and Robert kept an eye on its movements. You never know with big black Bouviers.

After the chilly walk along the river it was a welcome change to enter the cozy farmhouse. The wife of the farmer was feeding four young children seated around a large square table in the middle of the room.

"Nel, look we have a couple of guests for the night." Nel looked at her husband and shook her head.

"You know we decided never to take in any soldiers. What made you decide to take them without my permission?"

The farmer raised his hand to hush her. "These guys are from the Resistance. They came all the way from The Hague to find out about the troop movements of the Canadians. They are dressed like Canadian soldiers so they will be able to get around at the front lines. So I decided to help them. You know we always have helped the Resistance and the Jewish fugitives, Nel."

When Kees heard the word 'Jews' he had a dozen questions to ask but he waited for a more opportune time to do so. After the children have gone to bed, we'll have plenty of time for that, he decided.

The wife was still skeptical about the two visitors. "What if the Nazis have seen them coming; they'll come and shoot us tomorrow."

"Hush, Nel. The Nazis are nowhere to be seen and the war will be over in a matter of days anyway with all the thousands of paratroopers which arrived two days ago."

Little did she know, and for the time being that was a good thing, how long it would be before freedom would actually arrive in her beloved country. How long would she have to pretend to be a neutral citizen who would not be on any party's side? How long would she have to pretend that there were no guests at her Bed and Breakfast?

The evening went by fast. After the children had been put to bed, the four people were talking about everything that had gone on since the Canadians had landed. Their hidden radio had been turned on and a special broadcaster from the Canadian Army was telling the citizens to stay out of the battle zone.

There was no other news; the presses had stopped their printers until the Germans would be defeated in order to keep the Nazis in the dark about the actions of the liberators. There was only one newspaper issued that day. The farmer had picked up a copy at the ferry. *'Volk and Vaderland'* (Citizens and Homeland) was the Dutch translation, but it was printed under supervision of the Nazis and all the information was Nazi propaganda.

The headline read:

Infiltrating Canadian Enemy Destroyed

A few Canadian parachutists who landed south of Arnhem, have been shot and killed, the ones who surrendered have been taken into captivity. The enemy did not have a chance against our mighty forces. Citizens are urged to stay home and not give into the temptation to hide any of the foreign soldiers. If they are caught hiding fugitives their house will be burned and citizens will be incarcerated and tried by Stand Recht.

On another page a large ad was telling the Citizens with the headline:

Arbeits Einsatz

Any man over the age of 16 and under 65 has to report to the nearest Arbeits office. They will be put to work in the trenches, digging and reinforcing our frontlines around Arnhem. Any male person in the aforementioned age group who is found in their house or on the streets will be taken into custody.

The newspaper was giving the impression that everything was as usual and that the Nazis were still in charge. In two weeks they would be proven right.

When Kees and Robert left the next morning they were anxious to find out for themselves what the real truth was. They walked back to the ferry and hitched a ride from an army vehicle towards the front lines. That night they heard the battle rage and saw the flames from burning buildings all over the city. They heard the sirens from afar warning the remaining citizens of Arnhem about approaching planes, whether from the Canadians or the Nazis. They could also hear the anti airplane cannons shoot at the bombers flying over.

It was difficult to sleep in the tumult of warfare, even while it was miles away. The thought that at any time a bomb could drop on the farm or a plane hit by anti-aircraft guns could drop on the house was a danger they had forgotten about after four years of occupation. This was real warfare all over again and the citizens were tired and afraid. Would it ever end? Would the Nazis ever be defeated? How many would have to die, how many would have to lose their homes and their lives before an honest to goodness liberation would come about?

The insecurity drove people insane. The hunger drove people outside their homes in search of some food and even of water. The water works of the cities around Arnhem had been turned off. In too many bombed houses the pipes had burst and precious water streamed all over the streets.

The German occupation had closed down the water supply two weeks earlier. The citizens were boiling water from the rivers in order to be able to use it, but they would also have to find fuel to be able to boil anything.

The Jeep which took the two Resistance delegates, Kees and Robert, to the front lines of the battle had to get off the road several times. German Messerschmitt would fly over low and shoot at anything that was moving. Kees began to feel the intensity of the war going on. He determined to get his mission accomplished quickly and get out of the activities that could lead them to an imminent death.

When they arrived at the school that had been requisitioned by the Canadians for use as their temporary headquarters, he could not believe how many soldiers were guarding the complex. All around the school anti-aircraft cannons were set up. The sound of constant shooting tore apart the peace that once pervaded the normally quiet school grounds. One had to shout to be heard. Kees was led inside and downstairs into a large basement. At the far end of the basement a row of lockers had been used to partition off the desks of the Generals in charge of the offensive.

Kees had left Robert at the entrance of the building. He thought it would be wise to not overwhelm the Canadians and burden them with unnecessary security checks. When Kees had been announced by the Ordinance who had ushered him to the, what seemed chaotic headquarters, the General in charge greeted him cordially.

"So you came from The Hague's Resistance headquarters to find out about our progress," was his first remark as they shook hands.

Kees nodded and said, quite to his own surprise, in a military manner, "Yes, Sir." The General laughed about a citizen's efforts to act like military. He invited Kees to sit down at the improvised desk made of two doors, which had been pulled off their hinges. He shuffled with some maps and bent over them, inviting Kees to look at them as well.

"Unfortunately, Mr.van Rijn, we are in a very awkward position here." He pointed at a place on the map and continued, "The Nazis are here, here and there and we have only one way out or in. We are short of supplies and ammunition. Every night we have been getting some by means of drop shipments from gliders, but it is not enough. We have already lost nine hundred men and we cannot expect reinforcements from the Yankees in time. They are held up in Luxemburg right now, and it will take too long for them to arrive."

We can hold this position for four more days and, if a miracle does not happen, we will have to withdraw or we will lose this battle completely, along with many men. We don't want to give the Nazis that kind of satisfaction but we may have to, in order to regroup at the border of Belgium and wait until the Allies catch up with us.

As a thundering sound interrupted the conversation, he pulled Kees to the ground and both of them dove beneath the improvised table. "That was a bomb and it must have hit somewhere on the school grounds." Soldiers came rushing in and told the General where the hit had landed. Luckily there were no casualties. To be hit by a bomb in broad daylight was showing that the enemy was getting too close for comfort. The General left and told Kees to stay where he was.

He returned just a moment later and pulled Kees from under the table. "Mr. van Rijn, I don't know what to tell you at this moment, but please leave here as soon as you can and tell your friends in The Hague that the liberation of Holland will take a while longer. We are going to withdraw for reasons I gave you earlier, and only God knows when we will be able to attack the Nazis again. This offensive has to end right now or we will lose many more brave soldiers."

When Kees left, he was very disappointed. At last the Canadians came to free his country and they were defeated because they were not strong enough. Now what was going to happen? He dreaded to take this news to The Hague. The near future would become the worst winter of the war. How many of his fellow citizens would have to die of hunger and cold?

They could not find a lift to take them back to the ferry so the two began to walk the four kilometers along the Rijn River. It was mid morning on a crisp, early fall day in September 1944. The fields did not know, nor did the cows in them know, how great of a suffering was ahead of them. No one knew how long they could keep up the tension of shortages and no food at all. How long could every Hollander bear the pressure of the oppressors? What else would the Nazis come up with to make their lives even more miserable? These big questions hung in the fresh air and ruined the beauty of nature. How long? HOW LONG?

The Americans are coming! But when?

They reached the ferry at midday and went to the post where their German uniforms had been kept waiting until their return. The sergeant looked up from his field phone and did not look all too happy. "You must have heard the big news of our withdrawal before I did," he stated. "That must be a shock to you and your people. Now it is back to the underground trenches. I hope it will not take too long for you. You can count on this – we will be back!"

It was of little consolation. The liberators' intentions were good, but, oh, if they only knew what kind of hell existed on the other side of the river.

Kees felt ashamed to dress up in his Nazi uniform. The people on the ferry were looking at the two of them and they could see the suspicion in their eyes. Were they two Nazis who had been spying on the Canadian liberators? When they said their goodbyes to the captain of the ferry, it seemed all eyes were pointed at them.

They found the ambulance in one of the barns owned by the ferry company. When they drove away Kees sighed, "We better go to Oosterbeek before we return to The Hague. I need to warn our friends there that freedom is not here yet."

Chapter Eight

THREE EXTRAORDINARY PEOPLE MEET

An hour later Kees was knocking on the same beam at the demolished fire station he had knocked on just the week before. The same procedure brought the people in the open. To his great delight, Kees saw a familiar face coming towards him. It was an unexpected surprise that almost made Kees shout. At the last split second he restrained himself. Instead he whispered, "Levi, what are you doing here?"

The answer was rather ironic."Dominee de Groot, at your service."

Because of all the events of the last few days it had escaped Kees. What had happened to the Rabbi? He was very interested in what kind of experiences the Jewish Levi had encountered. Kees shook his hands and pulled him towards the fire truck out of which a number of faces had been watching the scene. They were all delighted to see him so soon again and they fired numerous questions at him.

"Kees, are we going to be free soon? Is the war almost over? Where can we go when we get out of here?" And so on.

Kees raised both hands in the air. "Not so fast, you all. I can't answer that many question at one time. Let's get inside here and sit down to talk, because a lot of things are happening and not too many are good ones."

Some of their smiling faces turned into a look of shock when they heard the words Kees spoke. Once they were seated Kees began, "My dear friends, I just came from the frontlines near Arnhem and I spoke with the General of the Canadians who is leading the offensive." He waited several minutes to continue, weighing his words carefully, because he knew what the disappointment could do to their minds, especially at this time of the war.

"The offensive by the Canadians has failed." He could see shock on the faces of his friends but then they began to ask question again, all of them at the same time. Kees waved his hand once more, demanding silence and went on. "They had expected the Allies to be here by this time and they would have certainly won this offensive if they had had greater strength. The Americans are tied up in Luxemburg. The fighting there is taking so much longer because of the mountainous terrain. They don't expect to be finished in Luxemburg for at least a month. If the Canadians had enough men here they could have held their position. They lost more than nine hundred soldiers and they are practically surrounded. They are retreating towards the Belgium border tonight."

Soft sounds of regret could be heard in the inside of the fire truck. Dominee De Groot took the initiative to speak.

"My dear friends, I know this is a shock, but I did not know about it either. You can see that it is wise not to jump to conclusions when it comes to warfare. The Nazis are still strong but they have awakened the sleeping giant of the world and soon, yes very soon, they will be defeated. You have survived thus far and God will give you strength to keep going. It may even become more difficult and it may be harder to get food. But at least you are alive and safe here. Come, let us pray together and ask the Lord for a safe retreat for the Canadians and for endurance for all of us in the next weeks to come."

It had become very quiet in the belly of the fire truck when they all bowed their heads and participated in the former Rabbi's prayer. When he ended they made a collective sigh and began to praise the Rabbi for his prayer and support.

They did not seem too surprised about his conversion. When he had arrived, he had done the same thing he had always done at all the other hiding places. He had begun with the questions. Why did the people who were hiding them do it and what was motivating them? The answers had been surprising to him. Every time the Jewish people said it was because their hosts believed they are God's chosen people and that Jesus of Nazareth gave them the strength to do it.

All the people in the fire truck remained silent for a long time. Finally Kees spoke, "The reason I came today was to warn you all to stay put, especially in the days ahead. The Nazis might go crazy once they take charge again. For now I have to leave and I don't know when I will see you again. May God bless you, sustain you and give you strength and wisdom. Shalom, my friends."

When Kees began to leave, Levi, alias Dominee De Groot, followed him and asked, "Is there any place where we can talk, just you and me, Kees? Do you know a safe address here in the area?"

Kees nodded, "Yes, a very great place and also a place where I want you to meet someone else. There is a small farm on the Estate of Baron van Boetselaer in Mariendaal. The farmer is against hiding Jews and he supplies the Nazis. It is the perfect place to have a meeting without any suspicion."

"It is there that I want you to meet a hero, a Jew, an awesome man."

The ambulance was parked in the same abandoned warehouse as before. The two friends walked inside and minutes later the ambulance rolled out. The neighbors wondered what the German ambulance was doing in their area. They had not heard any shots close by nor had they seen any Nazis for hours.

It took just ten minutes to reach the farm of Krelis van Houten. When the ambulance drove up to his house he looked totally surprised. What was going on now? An ambulance, a Nazi one at that? It had no business at his little peaceful farm. Then he saw the face of Kees, who was in a German uniform and now he really began to wonder what on earth was going on. Kees laughed at the confused farmer, "Guten tag, Herrn Krelis." (German for, "Good day, Mr. Krelis.") They both had to laugh at the odd scene, and that broke the ice. Then Robert, the driver, also clad in a German uniform got out and lastly the Rabbi. Kees introduced both the men as his colleagues. "This is my driver and friend in the Resistance and Dominee De Groot, who wanted to keep me company for the afternoon.

"I would like to inform you here at the farm, about the offensive that is going on and about the possible end of the war. Unfortunately, the war is going to continue for who knows how long. The Canadians are losing their shirts and are retreating tonight. The Nazis are reinforcing their armies around Arnhem and I have received information that all the troops which have been coming by here from the west of the country are going to be replaced with fresh troops in the next few days."

They were still talking in front of the house when the Krelis' farmhand appeared from the stable. When he saw Kees and his driver he turned his back to them and went back inside. He had recognized both Kees and the Rabbi and wondered what was being played out there in front of the house. Arriving in a German ambulance was odd enough, dressed up in German clothes was more than strange, and lastly, having a Rabbi with them was the epitome of weirdness.

Arie trusted Kees and the Rabbi and did not want to compromise them by confronting the two people he had known throughout the entire war. He hoped he would get a chance to talk to both soon.

Perhaps he could lure Krelis away from them for awhile. He began to think of a way to do just that and then he thought of something that could do the trick. He was going to spook the horse, the only work horse which Krelis owned that was used for plowing, cultivating and grading the fields, as well as drawing the carriage to the city. He decided to spook that horse and allow it to escape from the stable, through the back door.

The three visitors were still talking to Krelis about the war and the defeat of the Canadians when a loud bang sounded in the barn. It was so loud that it spooked the horse, which broke loose from its rope and galloped out the back door.

Krelis came running to the stable and yelled, "What happened, did you break something?" At the same time he took off after the galloping horse, which by then was running half a kilometer away from the farmhouse. Arie attempted to follow Krelis, but he called out to him, "Stay where you are and keep an eye on those visitors."

Slowly and casually Arie walked up to the visitors with his back to the running Krelis. He greeted the Rabbi and Kees.

"What on earth are you two, or three, up to coming here like this? We are suppliers of the Nazis and sometimes they come and pick up stuff here. Perhaps you two, he pointed at the Rabbi and Kees, should come inside the stable and stay out of sight. The driver should stay in the ambulance so if the Germans come he would have the excuse that he drove by here to ask for some milk and cheese. That is normal. It happens all the time, and certainly an ambulance from the west might have dropped off a wounded military in Germany."

They did as he asked and walked into the stable. The minute they were inside, Arie closed the door behind them and embraced both visitors. "How exciting to see you together! I did not even know you knew each other."

"This is the man I wanted you to meet Levi, but I did not know that you knew each other." Levi began to explain, but as he was talking they heard the galloping of the horse with Krelis on its back outside the stable. When he came inside leading the horse to its stall, Arie apologized for spooking the horse. While he was speaking they heard the sound of an engine coming up towards the house.

This farm did not have a gate which had to be opened. Anyone wanting to come to the house could do so at any time. This had been one of the reasons why Krelis could do business with the Nazis. The truck that was coming to a stop in front of the stable had at least six German soldiers in the back, while the sergeant was riding in the front with the driver. Arie quickly ushered the Rabbi and Kees up to the hayloft. Krelis approved of it and warned, "Better not have any incidents here or I will lose them as my valued customers, and even my freedom could be at risk. Hide them upstairs, Arie, and I will go talk to them. Hopefully they are not here to search my farm."

Krelis went to greet the Germans and addressed the sergeant by his first name. "Guten tag, Franzl, how are you today? What brings you to my little farm? Any particular needs?"

The sergeant had turned to his soldiers and commanded them to stay in their seats. That was a good sign for Krelis. At least they were not there for a search. "We are looking for some meat for tonight. Do you have anything we can buy from you, Krelis? I know you have not slaughtered a cow lately, but maybe you'll have some rabbits or chickens. We need to create a welcome and victory dinner tonight for two Generals who are coming in from Berlin and no one has anything in their store." Krelis felt benevolent this day, not because he liked his clients, but because he knew they would not visit him too many more times. The war would come to an end one of these days.

"I'll tell you what I will do for you today, Franzl. For your special dinner I will slaughter a calf. I was planning to do it anyway in a week or two. It will cost me a dozen pounds less meat. But for your occasion, I will make an exception."

The Sergeant asked, "How much will that special treatment cost me?"

"I will charge you the regular price of ten guilders per pound. Just tell me how many pounds you want." The deal was made for twenty pounds of veal, the favorite meat for the Germans.

Krelis thought that if he could only put enough cyanide in it and get away with it, that it might help shorten the war. The thought was dismissed immediately. Krelis was no killer and he was not military either. The deal was made and paid for with the message to come and get it in three hours. The German truck left with its soldiers. A threat was turned into a profit-making proposition.

Meanwhile, the three men in the hayloft above the stable had been able to have their talk. Arie was asking the Rabbi and Kees if they could bring his sister, who lived in The Hague, to him. He had written her a letter and Kees was willing to take it to her.

"The problem is, Arie, transportation is getting very difficult. I do not always have the ambulance available. Perhaps in the coming weeks something might come up that would enable me to bring your sister.

"No one knows what is going to happen in the West. Rumors are going around that the Germans are sending lots of fresh troops in airplanes to land at Ypenburg. That is the headquarters for our ambulances like the one we used today. We don't know if we can keep using them or if, God forbid, we get caught with them one of these days. So, my friend, keep praying that things will work out for us as well as for your sister. I will do my best; no promises".

"One more question, Arie." The Rabbi asked, "Does your sister have an Ausweiss without a red 'J' on it?"

"I don't know, but perhaps Kees could take care of that detail?"

Chapter Nine

WAR AND RETREAT

It was time for the farmer to slaughter a calf. It was the best fatted calf that he could supply, considering the shortage of the right nourishments. *It will have to do,* he thought to himself. Krelis did not have any time to entertain his guests and he told them so.

"I will have to get to work, gentlemen, and I will need my farm hand to help me with this job; please excuse me."

The three visitors stepped into the ambulance and went on their way.

"I left my bicycle at the fire station," said the Rabbi, "so I wonder if you can give me a ride back to The Hague."

"We'll have to hide your bicycle underneath the gurney, put you on the stretcher and cover your face up with some bandages. I don't have any transportation papers in case we get stopped, but they hardly look at those anyway. We can say that we picked you up on our way back from Germany at the battle in Arnhem and that you are going to a hospital in The Hague." The plan had been laid out, though the execution would be quite different.

When they rode into the town of Oosterbeek it seemed like the war had begun all over again. Tanks and army trucks were travelling towards the West again in great numbers. The encroaching Nazis used every inch of the roadways to move their equipment and men to the earlier abandoned western part of Holland. At the same time masses of fugitives from the city of Arnhem were moving in the same direction, blocking the roads for the enemy. Honking their horns to move out of the way was useless. The fugitives were pushing and hauling all kinds of improvised vehicles made of baby carriages, wheelbarrows and even office chairs on rollers. An old lady was pulling a very old man on a wagon, which was loaded up with a stack of gunnysacks. It was perhaps their entire possession.

The ambulance moved along with the other German vehicles as if it were one of them. On rare occasions Robert, the driver, would turn on his lights and siren, just to move past a clutter of German and civilian contraptions which were unable to go forward.

There was also the imminent danger of the Hunter airplanes and Messersmitts chasing and shooting each other causing everyone on the road to jump into the ditches. Even the Germans went into the ditches when the planes came roaring over. Occasionally a plane was shooting at the traffic on the road. It was hard to tell if they were friend or foe by what they were aiming at.

They had been on the road for three hours, and could have been home by then, but they had travelled only five kilometers.

Kees remarked, "This is going to take us into curfew and I wonder if the Nazis will let the fugitives walk, or if they will chase them away. We will be ok in our German ambulance, except for the chance that they will create check points somewhere."

Suddenly a plane came roaring right towards the road. A large plume of smoke came from the fuselage. Kees screamed above the noise of the roaring engine, "Stop and jump," but it was too late. The plane sheared right over their ambulance. They could hear its tail scratch the roof of the truck and then it tumbled over behind them, on top of a Nazi truck loaded with soldiers. Instantly the plane exploded and caused the army truck to explode in one great ball of flames.

Everyone else had jumped into the ditches. The grass and the bushes near the fire began to burn as well, and the people hiding beneath the dyke began to run and scream. They fled in all directions leaving their paltry possession behind.

Robert regained his composure and yelled to Kees, "What should we do now? After all we are supposed to be Germans and by driving a German ambulance we should see if we can help." They could not see what was behind the ball of fire, whether it be civilian fugitives or Nazis.

"There is no way we can save any of the victims in the army truck. The only thing I really want to do is find out whose plane it was that crashed; if it was a German or a Canadian plane which crashed and caused this accident."

The answer to that question came sooner than Kees had expected. In the field just down the road they noticed a man wrestling with a parachute, he had apparently released his harness but he was obviously caught in a spider net of ropes. Kees yelled to the driver, "Keep going and I'll go and help the poor guy; hopefully he is a Canadian."

When the pilot saw a German soldier emerge from the ambulance he thought his freedom had come to an end. Kees called to him in German, which made the case seem worse for the pilot but he felt he had to keep up appearances in case any Germans could hear him. Kees ran as fast as he could and when he reached the pilot he saw that he was indeed a Canadian. Under his breath he said in English, "I am from the Dutch Resistance, but since I am dressed as a German I am going to have to arrest you and take you with me in my ambulance. Don't worry, you will be safe."

He grabbed the pilot by his jacket and pulled him out of the 'spider web' of ropes. Holding him roughly by his jacket, he pushed the man towards the approaching ambulance. The road around the fire had been cleared. All the fugitives were somewhere in the fields and then Kees noticed that there were no Germans close by. He said to the pilot, "The Lord has rescued you miraculously. Come let's get out of here quickly before the Nazis catch up with us."

As soon as the two men had jumped into the ambulance, it sped away, but not for long, as they covered only a few hundred meters and then were stuck in traffic again. The pilot was stunned and confused. He was sitting in the back of the ambulance. The German on the gurney was talking English to him and he did not seem wounded at all, despite all the bandages around his head. After a few minutes he began to ask questions.

The man on the gurney had introduced himself as Dominee Henk de Groot, "It means Pastor," he explained, "And to make it even more difficult for you, I just converted from being a Jewish Rabbi to become a Christian. I travel around the hiding places all over this country and minister to the Jews in hiding."

"So what is this disguise in German uniforms and in a German ambulance all about?" He demanded to know.

"Kees, the person who rescued you is one of the leaders of the Resistance. He had to go to your people in Arnhem to find out about the progress of the offensive by our liberators. In The Hague they have already celebrated the liberation but the Resistance needed to know if it was for real. Many Nazis had left the city of The Hague when the people took to the streets. The Nazis and the Dutch traitors got scared and began to run towards Germany. The Resistance felt that before we would begin to act as if we had been liberated, we wanted to be sure of it for obvious reasons.

"As you probably know by now, the Canadian Offensive failed and the troops have withdrawn from Arnhem to the Belgian border to join the Allies there. You must have been in the air to defend and cover their retreat. So, were you shot down or did your plane fail?"

The pilot acknowledged that he had been shot by a Messersmitt. He had tried to land in the fields next to the road. At the last minute, he had been able to abort his plane.

They drove for two kilometers when all traffic came to a complete stop. From all directions Nazi vehicles had come together. Huge pile-ups had made passing completely impossible. Even for their ambulance there was no room to pass through. A stream of vehicles coming from the west packed with the most impossible household goods; trucks full of cattle, farmers' tools, bicycles, anything the Nazis had looted from the citizens in the West was being hauled to Germany. From all other directions tanks, cannons, people movers and jeeps with soldiers were trying to go back to the West; and in between all the traffic were the civilian fugitives on their way to find shelter for just one night.

Kees decided quickly that if they did not turn around, they too, would be stuck in the mess of human misery.

"Turn on the lights and the siren and turn around quickly or we will be stuck all night, and who knows what will happen?" The driver made his move. People had to jump away from the ambulance as it swerved around the criss-crossed vehicles. Within minutes it got clear of the jam and sped up on its way back to the village they had come from.

"I think we should either go back to the farm and sleep in the hayloft or find an abandoned house in the town of Oosterbeek."

Now they were with four people and Kees wondered if the farmer would welcome that many. When they drove in to Oosterbeek they saw a large two-story villa with its windows shot out and its front door wide open. In the back of the villa was a garage with its door also open. It seemed a possibility for them to stay there.

It was amazing that the Nazis had not occupied this villa. In the days before the offensive they had come to the village and simply rang the doorbell or shot the door open to any house they needed for their war efforts. They would trample the neatly kept floors with their dirty army boots, grab whatever they wanted and ruin the personal effects of the owners without any respect.

Kees' group got settled in, hid the ambulance in the garage and closed the doors. They found some planks and barricaded the broken windows.

"Now what?" asked Kees, "I wish I had a radio so we could find out what is happening. We should stay put here until we know. Apparently, the Canadians are still around because I hear the shooting of machine guns and cannons.

There are still Canadian planes in the air; so how can we find out when it is safe to go back home?"

The Rabbi had an idea. "Why don't you use my bike to ride to the farm Kees? The farmer might have a radio and perhaps he can tell what the situation is."

"That is a good idea," Kees agreed. But he addressed the pilot, "You better stay prepared to go into hiding. Even here in this house the Nazis have a habit of showing up at any time of the day, taking possession of a house or coming in and searching a house for fugitives or Jewish people. So Levi, can you assist the pilot here and find a good hiding place for him and figure out the quickest way to get to it, just in case?"

At the Canadian Headquarters on the other side of the river Rijn, troops were feverishly packing up all their equipment. The corps of engineers was-breaking down tents and loading up their tools. The night before, they had not been able to leave their position because of the multiple attacks from the Nazis.

The Canadians had been able to keep them from getting closer and for a moment the General in charge had thought of staying. But the high command had ordered him out of there and after all the attacks and the heavy cannon fire, he had given the command to pack up in the very early morning. That evening under the guidance of a large number of airplanes and the cover of darkness, they were going to make their move. The plan was in place and the defenders in their planes were ready to hit the airspace south of Arnhem and guide their troops to safety.

That night would become the noisiest night Kees and his friends had ever experienced during the four years of war. They were down in the basement of the villa in fear of a bomb hitting the house. That fear became very justified when around midnight a loud bang woke up all four and they heard the roof of the villa cave in. They did not dare go up the stairs from the basement, fearing that there might be a fire raging above.

"It must have been a fighter plane," the Canadian pilot remarked. " I heard the roar of an engine before it crashed."

They waited a long fifteen minutes in the basement. It seemed completely silent and from above no other noises could be heard, other than the regular staccato sounds of machine guns. They did not smell the scent of a fire nor did they hear any of the sounds that would betray that a fire was in progress. Carefully they went up the stairs. The door to the basement was stuck, and the three of them pushing it realized they could not open it.

They decided to break the door and, if that worked, they would be able to see what was blocking it. Kees went back down into the basement and looked for an object that he could use to demolish the door. He found a shovel and a regular hammer and took them both to the landing where the staircase began its descent. It took them a long time to create a hole in the solid oak door to finally be able to look at what was behind it. A huge pile of debris, wood, roof tiles and beams were blocking the door. It would not be an easy job to break out of this predicament.

While three men were working on demolishing the door, Kees had gone back down to the basement. He remembered that houses build in the late eighteen hundreds usually had an exit from the basement to the garage. If that was the case he was determined to find it. It was dark in the basement; only a tiny vent which was connected to the ceiling shed a little light into the basement. The walls were covered with boxes and built-in cabinets. Perhaps a door was hidden somewhere behind the cabinets. Kees began to move the boxes first. They were all full with magazines and newspapers. Apparently they had not lacked fuel in this villa yet.

Upstairs on the landing they were still banging away on the heavy oak door. It was too thick to make a dent in it. They were working at the small hole which had given them a peek at the debris behind it. Determined not to give in, the three men kept banging and pulling. Splinter by splinter the pieces came off. Meanwhile, Kees had moved most of the boxes away from one wall when he found a door. It was covered with spider webs and had apparently not been opened for years. When Kees pulled the door handle it fell to the ground along with the board that had held the door lock. He pulled at the rest of the door. With a loud squeak it opened. What he saw did not surprise him, partially caved-in walls with daylight coming through thick bushes that were covering the exit at the end of a long hallway.

Kees cried out and Levi yelled back, "What did you find?"

"The way out," Kees shouted back. "Stop what you are doing and come on down." The three men came thundering down the staircase and saw what Kees had discovered. They slapped Kees on the back with joy. For a moment they had forgotten what time it was and what situation they had found themselves in. They walked the long tunnel, which had so obviously not been used for perhaps fifty years, and entered a small stairway with only six steps leading outside to the back yard of the villa. The exit was right behind the double garage that was still completely intact.

Still a bit shaken Kees and Levi both agreed to say a prayer of thanks for their miracle of being alive. Robert prayed with the two men even though he was not a believer. To escape two plane crashes in one day was no accident.

Even to a non-believer, that had to be divine intervention. The Canadian pilot did not understand the language, but he certainly understood the solemn prayer of thanks Kees and Levi had spoken.

"Well, my friends, let's go and see who it was that paid us a visit during the last hour. Was it friend or foe? Let's see if there was a surviving pilot on the plane." It was not an easy task to reach the plane which had crashed into the roof, nose down, and had caused most of the roof to collapse. The heavy rafters had pulled down the walls of the house and the second floor had dropped onto the first floor.

The pilot's first reaction when he saw the plane was, "Oh, my Lord! It was one of my friends. I hope he got out on time." As he came closer to the cockpit by climbing on top of the debris, scattering pieces like a small avalanche, he let out an anguished cry, "Oh, no! He did not get out. Please Lord, have mercy on his soul.

"We need to get his body out of here," he yelled.

Kees moved closer to him and put his finger to his lips. "Quiet, no one knows we are here. Let's keep it that way," he whispered. The pilot realized what he had been doing and shook his head.

Continuing Kees' example, in a whisper, he said, "I will climb into the cockpit, loose my friend, and try to slide him down this rafter here." He raised his thumb for acknowledgement and Kees did the same. The other two men were lower than Kees. They would have to help catch the body and bring it outside into the back yard.

When all the work was done it had become early morning. The fighting in the sky and on land had subsided and a restful time finally set in. But for Kees and his three friends, the end of their struggle was not yet near. They had to take care of the body of the pilot who had crashed his plane on the villa. Could they follow the retreating Canadians to the Belgian border? Certainly they could not take it to The Hague where the Nazis still reigned? The four men discussed the situation and decided by mutual agreement that they should follow the route the Canadian Army had taken until they could catch up with them. They would reach two goals that way: the body would be in the proper hands and the living pilot would be back to work with his proper outfit.

Kees made the final arrangements, "We will take two hours of sleep. We can all sleep in the ambulance, and one of us will keep watch. We will store the body in the tunnel we came out of from the basement until we leave." With that, they all took their seats in the ambulance. Levi volunteered to take the watch.

Two hours later Kees was wide awake and he did not want to alarm the other sleepers. The responsibility he felt for the people he had with him weighed heavily on his shoulders. Perhaps that is why he had awakened so quickly. He looked at Levi, sitting on an old bench he had found on the patio. The ex-Rabbi must have wondered what kind of responsibility he felt towards them.

Softly, Kees walked towards Levi and whispered, "Levi, would you give me a hand with your bicycle? I am going to the farm nearby because I know they get up very early to milk the cows. I still need to find out what is going on in this part of the country and perhaps the farmer can give us tips as to how we should go to catch up with the Canadian forces."

Without speaking a word the two opened the door of the ambulance and lifted the bicycle out. The sleeping pilot just stirred and then went on to sleep. "He must have been exhausted. I'll be back within the hour," Kees said.

"Shalom, Levi." Kees jumped on the bicycle and was gone. He was the only *German soldier* on the streets thus was able to reach the farm without difficulty. Krelis and Arie were loading beet pulp on a wheelbarrow and brought it into the stables to feed the few cows and calves they still had on their little farm.

Surprised they looked up, and recognized Kees. Krelis remarked, "What brings you up here so early in the morning? I thought you would be back in The Hague by now."

Kees shook his head. "We tried to go and were about five hours on the road. We had moved only ten miles when we ran into the biggest mess I have ever seen. After waiting for a short time I decided to come back and stay for the night. We found a place to sleep, but in the middle of the night an airplane crashed on top of the villa. Luckily the ambulance was parked in the garage a little ways behind the villa and it did not get damaged. I wondered if you have heard anything on the radio about what is going on here with the retreat of the Canadians, or if you heard anything from the Germans?

"We need to know which way we should travel to avoid any fighting that is going on. Besides we rescued a Canadian pilot on the road yesterday and we have the body of the pilot who crashed into the villa as well. I thought we should try to catch up with the Canadians and deliver both to them and then go to The Hague. What you think?"

Krelis was thinking, meanwhile he continued to work. "I have never been involved in any war action on either side. In fact I have been trying to stay neutral during this entire war but, because I know you and the other gentlemen, and because you are both good people who are not using any guns here, this is what I suggest and how I can help." Kees was curious about what this simple farmer had in mind and waited patiently for his proposal.

"I have only one horse here and one carriage which I use to bring milk to the German garrison. My helper does that every day. He is unsuspected in the eyes of the Germans and has a special permit to ride around. Often he had been moving people who had to leave their house. The Germans have never bothered him. I am willing to have him take you to the Belgian border to where the Canadians are now. I heard on the radio this morning they have joined the Allied forces and they have endured a lot of attacks on their way. You must know that you have to go to the ferry ten miles south of here, cross the Rijn and head for Eindhoven, which is close to the Belgian border. From there is it only ten miles to the place where the Allied forces are.

"I am sticking my neck out for you and you must do what I tell you. Don't go dressed as German soldiers. I will give farmer's coveralls for the three of you. Go as soon as you can so my horse and wagon can be back here with you and your Dominee friend. You may stay here one more night. By then the road should be cleared for you to get to The Hague." Kees was impressed. This stubborn farmer had a heart after all.

Chapter Ten

THE BACKYARD FARM OF CORNELIUS

—∞—

The city was quiet. Many soldiers had left and so did many of the NSB-ers. The traitors had gone with their masters and had taken all their belongings, and many of their neighbors' possessions, as well. During the last two days, some of them had come back to their houses in the city. People were wondering why. The celebrations for the Liberation had stopped and fear had crept back into the citizens' minds. The police had driven around the city with loudspeakers on their cars and warned the people to stay inside their houses. The Nazi-supervised newspaper, the only war-time printed news source, *Volk and Vrijheid* (Citizens and Freedom) had announced in typical propaganda fashion that there was no liberation yet.

In this kind of atmosphere Johanna and Cornelius stayed inside the house at the Deiman Straat. Johanna struggled to find food for the twelve people she was hosting under the floor. Three times a day she would go to the local distribution center to see if there was any food. Only once did she receive two loaves of bread and a pound of butter. At home she still had a large can of beet syrup. The guests below would have to do with that for two days. Johanna was hoping Kees would come back that day. She had been hoping for his return for the third day now and the rumors of fighting had not helped to suppress her fear. She was grateful that Frans had come while the celebrations in the streets were going on. He had warned her, "Johanna, don't buy into the liberation stories yet; don't get involved in it. Stay at home and be sure not to let anyone see your guests from downstairs."

Cornelius was disappointed that he could not go outside and join the celebrations with his friends, but Johanna had insisted. "It is too dangerous with all these people dancing in the streets. As long as our government has not made the official announcement that we are free, we will act as though we are not."

He did not understand everything his mom had told him, and Uncle Frans had told him that his children were not allowed to go outside either. Cornelius had found his happiness in his little back yard farm. He had built a rabbit hutch out of two old suitcases. From an old stove grill he had made a front while the open back was standing against the stone wall of the house. He had brought some straw in the gunnysack when Marie gave him the rabbit at the Brandwijk farm. From his little back yard farm he took cabbage leaves and fed those to his big white Flemish giant. According to Marie, the babies should be born around the fifteenth of November. He could not wait another three weeks. Every day he went to feel the tummy of the rabbit; did it get bigger yet?

Marie had told him that he would have to dig up his potatoes at the end of the month. "Make sure that you dig them up no later than the first of October or your potatoes may begin to rot and you don't want to lose any," she had told him.

In August she had given him twenty kale plants and had explained to him that they would be the latest crop in is garden. "Kale plants can stand frost, so don't worry if they look frozen and icy one morning. It will make them taste better. Normally you plant kale in July, but at that time you told me you did not have any room, so I thought I would sow some new ones for you later."

Marie had become his personal teacher and he loved her like a big sister, perhaps even more. The next time he was going to the farm he planned to tell her about the marigolds he had sold on Frenzy Tuesday. He had collected over sixty guilders that day. He wanted to keep them growing for the next celebration of the liberation, if there would ever be one. That, too, he needed to discuss with his personal teacher, Marie.

Cornelius loved to be in his little back yard farm where he forgot about his hunger and did not have to think about his daddy who was somewhere in danger, doing things he was not allowed to tell anyone. He noticed how his plants were thriving on the pigeon manure he had scraped from the ledge on top of the Groenendijk warehouse. Poor Mister Groenendijk had lost most of his box bicycles when the Nazis raided his warehouse.

Cornelius remembered him coming back from the German headquarters where they had taken his bikes. He had been so mad that he was muttering to himself, "You cannot trust these Nazis. They are all thieves and I will never, ever, rent to them again." First they had stolen his pig and then they had stolen forty of his box-bicycles. He could not get any new ones and he could not make any because there was no wood, or wheels or any bicycle parts for sale anywhere in the city.

"Poor Mr. Groenendijk," his dad had said when he came home, "how is he going to live without renting his box-bicycles?"

Kees had gone to console Mr.Groenendijk. He had told him that he would get him some food from the farm now and then and that he could always count on him for anything he needed. He would find out later how valuable Kees's promise was to staying alive during the worst hunger winter of the war.

Cornelius saw his crop gradually getting smaller as the weather became colder. He was afraid that he would not have much food for his family and their guests during the coming winter and, if the Americans would not come soon, there would be no food at all.

He had heard his dad say to Mr. Groenendijk, "My son, Cornelius, has been such a blessing this year. Have you seen his little farm in the back yard?"

Mr.Groenendijk had laughed, "Yes, I have and I hear him every day on my roof. What on earth is he doing there?"

Diplomatically, Kees had answered, "You don't want to know," and with that they turned and went their separate ways.

In the large back yard of Mr. Groenedijk's warehouse he had kept all his box-bicycles every night. Now that the Nazis had stolen them, it was empty and weeds began to grow everywhere. Cornelius thought of the farm and how they mowed the weeds and fed them to the animals. He wondered if his rabbit would eat some of those weeds.

The fence between the two yards had been taken down during the last winter and used as firewood. Kees had carefully separated the planks and the poles and divided them in two stacks; one for him and one for Mr. Groenendijk. Both families had been able to keep their houses warm for two months.

Now Cornelius was able to step right into the neighbor's large storage yard and pull some of the weeds to see if his rabbit would eat them. One weed was tall and it had some kind of seed on it. He tried that first, but the rabbit would not touch it. *This rabbit is a picky one,* Cornelius thought, *it probably did not know that there was a war going on and that food could become very scarce.* Cornelius went back to the yard next door and pulled a dandelion plant. It had some big yellow flowers on it and he could almost bet that the rabbit would not eat that plant either. To his great surprise the rabbit ate it in a minute. Now that he knew what he could feed it, he determined in his little heart that he would find those plants for his rabbit.

In the back yard of the Deiman Straat there was not a very broad view of the sky. At first Cornelius heard the sound of airplanes. It sounded like there were many of them. Then he saw them. Many big planes filled the sky. The noise grew louder and louder until the entire sky was filled with planes. Cornelius ran inside and called out, "Mamma, Mamma, the whole sky is full of airplanes. Come and look! It sounds like there are thousands. Come, Mom."

Johanna had heard the noise. She had figured it was indeed the sound of planes. She followed her son out to the back yard and looked up. It looked as though the sky had been painted with large black specks and suddenly out of the planes came what seemed like hundreds of flies. As they came lower they looked like butterflies and then she realized what was happening. Thousands of parachutes were coming down out of the planes.

Were they people or things? Were they the Americans they had waited so desperately for or… .

"Oh, no," Johanna lamented, "Look, they have swastikas on their parachutes. Nazis! More Nazis are coming! There is no peace yet, oh, my dear, Cornelius, the war is starting all over again."

After a few more minutes the men landed on the streets, on the rooftops and two of them landed right on top of Cornelius' vegetables in his little garden. The soldiers simply said, "Guten tag" and asked to be led to the street as they were folding up their parachutes. They had damaged a lot of Cornelius' plants. All he could do was look in awe and horror at how they were stepping over and on top of them and pulling them out of the soil when the ropes hooked behind them.

At a certain time he could not stand the rude men any longer and yelled, "Hey, mister, be careful."

Johanna pulled him inside and told him to be quiet. "Those soldiers have guns and we don't want them to shoot us."

When it was all over they saw the thousands of soldiers neatly line up in columns and march away.

"How many have come, Mom?" Cornelius asked.

"I don't know, son. I think there must be many thousands."

The sky had cleared but the sound of many planes could still be heard. Slowly it ebbed away until it became eerily still. Mother and son watched the scene in front of the house as the troops had lined up. They were all young men; no one was older than eighteen, Johanna had observed. "Lord, have mercy on us and also on these young men who are coming to suppress us once more."

The people beneath the floor must have been wondering what had been going on. One of them was making the sound that they wanted to speak to someone. Johanna made up her mind to go down the ladder, through the sliding wall in the bathroom. All eyes were directed at her when she had come down. Just one of them spoke. They had learned not to make any noise and only the day leader could speak in a very soft voice.

"Johanna, what was all that noise all about?"

Johanna looked at them and a great feeling of sympathy came over her. These people had endured so much. They had hoped liberation was here a week ago. Now she would have to tell them that the war was going to continue; that new troops had arrived and that things might be getting worse because of the coming winter. It was all too much. Before she could utter a single word she began to cry. One of the ladies in the group of the hunted victims came and put her arm around her. She tried to speak soft words of encouragement.

The lady who was comforting her said to the others, "Let's all sit down and hold all our questions until she has calmed down. Obviously something horrible is happening and she will have to regain her strength to tell us."

It took a long time for Johanna to muster up the strength to tell them the truth. It was a terrible truth with huge consequences.

Finally she spoke. "What you heard was the sound of a new Nazi army coming down from the sky with parachutes. Thousands of them landed right here in the streets and even in our back yard, which made Cornelius upset because they damaged his garden.

"We all thought the war was over. Forget it. The Nazis brought in enough men to make our life miserable again. I really don't know what they are up to. Kees has been gone for days now and I don't even know how he is doing or where he is. All I know is, if God is for us, who can be against us?"

Ending with those words she felt strong again. She turned around and went on her way back upstairs again. She thought to herself, *If I did not have God in my life I would not want to live. I will talk to Kees when he comes home and suggest talking about salvation and believing in Jesus Christ to the guests down below. This would give them some of the power of Jesus to go through these times and survive in victory.*

Cornelius had been straightening up his back yard garden. Some of the cabbage plants had been trampled but he was able to salvage the small cabbage. *It should have grown two weeks longer,* he thought, but it would die if he left it all broken where it had been trampled. The leaves and even the trunks would be great food for his soon-to-be momma rabbit.

Johanna joined him is his cleanup efforts and softly spoke to him, "If it were not for Jesus, we would not be here, son. We are really the fortunate ones. We still have food every day."

"Not much," Cornelius interjected.

"We can be thankful for what we have or would you like to be like the people who live underneath our house? They cannot even come and breathe the fresh air out here."

Cornelius had to think about that. After a couple of minutes he agreed, "Mom, we are the fortunate ones."

Johanna's heart filled with great joy and thankfulness.

Chapter Eleven

BACK TO WAR AGAIN

—~~—

They had made good time on the farm carriage behind Krelis' steaming workhorse. The Jew without a star was having a great time; being free to ride through the landscape and talk to his former Rabbi and his former host from The Hague. They had passed the city of Eindhoven and were well on their way to the Belgian border when they encountered the first German barricade.

Arie had his papers and so did the Canadian pilot. He had borrowed the papers from the farmer, Krelis. The pictures were so vague that anyone could look like the person in the picture. Levi, the former Rabbi, had his papers with the name Dominee Henk de Groot. The trio was dressed in such a way that it looked acceptable to any Nazi. Hopefully they would not be searched, but if they were they had their story ready. After the usual, "Halt. Ausweisses," Dominee De Groot jumped off the wagon and showed his papers.

The Nazi Soldier looked at him sharply and said, "You are Dominee, what is your mission?"

Levi made a split second decision. *This guy seemed to be thorough so we better not hide anything here,* he thought. Then he launched his story. His two friends were farmhands who had stumbled upon a corpse in their fields. The man seemed to have been a pilot who had died there in the field. They had come to him to ask what they should do. I thought it humanitarian to bring the body of the man to his friends in the Canadian Army.

The Nazi soldier looked at the horse and carriage and then at the two farmhands and said, "Einem moment bitte."

He walked over to the Sergeant in charge of the barricade. The three saw him speak and then the Sergeant made a move with his hands. The two Nazis approached the wagon and demanded the Ausweisses of the two men on the front seat. The Sergeant looked at them briefly and then demanded to see the body of the pilot. Opening up the box of the wagon, they stared at the body for a second. The Sergeant said the desired words, "Gehen sie mahl." They were dismissed with a wave of his hand. The barricade opened up and they were on the road again.

"The Nazis seemed nervous," Kees remarked, "they must know that the Allies are close by and that they may soon lose their lives in a pending battle."

There were no more Germans in sight. There were no tanks or Nazi trucks on the rest of the way to Belgium. This was some sort of neutral zone between the two enemies. Without any further problems they came upon a long convoy of army trucks. They had formed an encampment with the trucks that covered the view of hundreds of tents. In the middle was a huge tent. They rode alongside the column of trucks until they saw an opening. Sentries were checking all traffic that was coming in. Their comical looking horse and carriage was out of place to be entering a military compound. Kees was the first one to speak. The Canadian pilot interrupted him before he had even begun.

"I am Canadian pilot Herman Brockenwites. Do you have a Canadian outfit here?"

Before he answered, the sentry said, "Sir, can I see your ID please?" The pilot produced it from the inside pocket of his pilot jacket which he had hidden underneath his seat and handed it to the sentry who looked at it for a moment before he answered the question.

"Sir, we do, yes but before I can let you in with your horse and carriage I will want to see the ID's of the others. I also need to check the contents of your carriage. We still remember the Trojan Horse you know."

They all laughed. What a different atmosphere it was here at the camp of the Allies.

The pilot spoke again and said, "We have the body of another Canadian pilot in the carriage. I will show you in a minute. We would like to deliver him to our Canadian doctors for a death certificate and hand him over for a proper burial or for shipping him back home."

"Gentlemen, I appreciate your attentiveness, but I will have to call an ambulance for the body and I would suggest you leave your horse and carriage here by the entrance and walk towards that big tent over there. You will find all the commands of the allied forces there. If you can wait just one moment I will send a soldier with you so you won't get lost."

Within minutes an American soldier arrived and escorted the three of them to the big tent. They walked into the command center and felt they were in a grand central station. People were everywhere and desks with flags on them indicated which country was represented there. The soldier led them directly through the multitude of military personnel, dressed in all kinds of different uniforms, towards the Canadian command. To his surprise Kees saw a man he had met just days before.

The General he had seen in Arnhem greeted him jovially saying, "Well, what do you know, you're the guy from the Resistance in Holland, aren't you?"

They shook hands and Kees introduced the other two. "This, sir is one of your pilots we picked up in the fields after he almost dropped his plane on top of us. And this, he pointed at Levi, is one of the few surviving Jewish Rabbis from Holland who has recently become a Christian."

"Wow," the general exclaimed, "that is amazing." He stretched out his hand towards Levi and said, "It is an honor to meet you sir. I would like to talk to you for at least an hour.

"Again, duty dictates that I will have to ask you what brought you here. I already know that you brought me back my pilot. Is there anything else I can do for you?"

The pilot answered the question, "Yes sir, we have also brought the body of a colleague of mine, another pilot, who unfortunately lost his life in a crash. He dropped his plane on top of a villa where we were staying and apparently failed to bail out on time. We were able to save his body and brought it here for the proper procedure. The Nazis stopped us and let us through, thinking we were some farmhands trying to do a good deed. The sentry at the gate took care of the body. He called an ambulance which supposedly took him to the morgue."

Kees asked the General if he could give him any information about the upcoming actions of the Allies.

"Of course", he replied with a smile. "I cannot give you any information other than it will happen soon, depending on the weather and the course of the battle of the Bulge, which is going on right now. Unfortunately it also depends on our mutual friend Herr Hitler."

The answer was vague and did not give much hope for the liberation soon, so Kees replied, "I understand your position and the inevitable secrecy which comes along with it; but you know there are ten million Dutch people out there who are suffering severely, along with fifty thousand Jews who are in constant threat of their lives."

It sounded bitter and the General noticed it. "I apologize , Mr. van Rijn. As

God is my witness I would love to be able to tell you that we are coming tomorrow, but you saw what happened to us just last week in Arnhem. We have to have everything in place to guarantee a victory."

The meeting had ended and the General stood up to shake everyone's hands. "May God be with you all, gentlemen, I wish you a safe trip back to Arnhem today."

Kees could not resist the tears welling up in his eyes. This man was so sincere and he knew he was doing what he could to get the country of Holland liberated.

He answered the General with the words, "Godspeed you and all the allies, and bless you all. Thank you for all you do." He shook hands with the General and felt a genuine friendship. "One last word, sir," he said, "I would love to see you after this is all over. You will always be welcome at my home in The Hague."

The horse ran as if it knew the way home and it smelled his stable. The barricade they passed on the way to Belgium was no longer there. The three travelers had rehearsed what they were going to say to the Nazis but they did not have to. Even when they reached the ferry going across the river there were no obstacles.

The ferry captain recognized Kees and asked him how his trip had been. "A farmhand, eh?" He could not resist making the remark, smilingly.

Kees answered him, "One needs to do whatever is necessary to survive in these days. Brace yourself my friend, this is going to be a long, cold and hungry winter." Softly, so no one could hear him Kees said, "The allies won't be able to free us until spring."

They reached the farm. Krelis had not expected them back that early. "You made good time back and forth. Everything all right?"

He was not a man of many words, but he showed his appreciation seeing them back without wasting time. Kees thanked him profusely and asked him if he could buy some milk and cheese to take to the city.

"You can take some free if you will deliver some to my sister on Borneo Street in The Hague." Kees affirmed he would and they began to load up the hidden ambulance and wake up Robert, the driver.

An hour later they were on their way to The Hague once more. Cheese, butter and milk were hidden, together with the fancy decorated bike of Levi, in the space, where Jewish people had often been hidden, under the double floor of the ambulance. Kees and Robert had dressed themselves up in Nazi uniforms and Levi was wrapped up as a patient on the gurney.

The German ambulance drove all the way to Utrecht without incidence.

The trouble began just when they had passed the city. A stream of people, fugitives, who had walked for days from the battle zone around Arnhem, blocked the roads once again. Kees had expected to be home that evening but he saw the chance of that quickly disappear. The small towns west of Utrecht had been overwhelmed with the numbers of people seeking a roof over their heads for the past two nights. This day was no different.

Levi knew of a farm just down the road where he had visited a group of Jews several times. "Let's see if we can stay there for the night and then we should try to leave at the crack of dawn tomorrow morning to see if we can get ahead of the crowd." They almost forgot that they were driving a German ambulance.

Among the crowds on the village roads there were no Germans. No army vehicles had been in this village for a few weeks. The ambulance was riding around and receiving the scorn of many of the fugitives. Little did they know that their protectors were riding past them. The fugitives were asking the villagers for a place to sleep for just one night. All the houses and stables were filled to the brim with people. As long as everyone could just lie down, no matter where they were, they were hoping to be safe.

When the ambulance entered the gates of the farm, two large black Bouvier dogs came running towards them. No one dared to get out of the German vehicle until the farmer came walking towards the ambulance. Not very friendly, he demanded to know what they were doing at his farm. When he noticed Levi he changed his tune a little. Levi had pulled the bandages from his face and had come off the gurney. Still sounding hostile, he must have thought the Nazis had arrested Levi when Levi spoke.

"Johannes Verburgh, I see you remember me. Don't be afraid of what you see. I have two Resistance members with me who have undergone quite an ordeal in the last few days. We have come back from the front lines and were able to gather a lot of valuable information. We are now on our way back to The Hague, but we got stuck here in the stream of fugitives and need a place to stay for the night."

The farmer seemed relieved and said, "I was shocked to see a German vehicle. A few weeks ago they came by from the West and robbed whatever they could here at the farm. They even stole my horse and two carriages and filled them with whatever they could grab. I was not going to let that happen this time. With one command the dogs would have torn you apart. I have trained them that way. The usual Nazis which had occupied the village before they all fled to Germany knew that, so they never bothered me."

At that moment he shouted a harsh command and the dogs turned around and, with their tails between their legs, the two vicious animals went back to their dog house.

Levi introduced Kees and Robert and together they went inside the farm house. Once in the visitors' room of the farm, the farmer's wife came walking in. At first she was as confused as her husband had been. The farmer spoke up when he saw the look on his wife's face.

"Anna, this is Rabbi Levi, remember? And the other two are with the Resistance from The Hague. They have been on a mission at the front lines near Arnhem and that is why they are dressed in Nazi uniforms and driving a Nazi ambulance. God forbid they would ever get caught in their disguise."

Anna became who she normally was – the hospitable gentle farmer's wife. She offered them soup and bread. She even apologized for the simple meal she was able to put before them.

Both Levi and Kees were anxious to find out if they were still hiding Jews at the farm. Kees posed the question, "How many Jews are you hiding here at your farm?"

At first Johannes looked at Levi. They could see the question on the farmer's face, wondering if he should answer that question.

Levi merely nodded his head and said, "It's all right Johannes, Kees happens to be the head of the Jewish hiding department in The Hague. I was surprised that he did not even know that you used to have Jews here. You do, don't you?"

This time the farmer nodded. "Yes, but I only have six, because a week ago ten of them left for a farm North of Utrecht. They had been picked up by a group from Utrecht." Kees asked for the name of the group. "Pins, I believe," the farmer answered.

When that name had been uttered, Kees gave a shout, "Pins, you said?" Adrie Pins was an NSB-er who was notorious in The Hague. He searched out Jewish hiding places and betrayed them to the Nazis for money. "He is the meanest rat in the country. Oh, God, have mercy on our Jewish friends".

Levi who had been listening to the shocking conversation remarked, "You need to get those six out of here right now, Johannes. We cannot waste a minute because this Mr. Pins could come back any moment. Then he might take you and your wife as well."

"I have a small laborer's house a kilometer from here in the meadows," Johannes interjected with a fearful sound in his voice. "It is used to stock food for my livestock. It has an attic with hay in it and six people can certainly stay there."

Kees took the initiative. "Where are they? Let's go, we have no time to lose. Behind the crowd of fugitives a new German army is coming and we don't know how mean they are going to be."

It took them five minutes to get the group of hidden Jews together with their minimal belongings and disappear in the night. The walk through the wet grass and the darkness surrounding the group of driven and hunted Jews with their protectors took only twenty minutes. When they safely entered the little house Kees and Levi let out a sigh of relief. "This might have been the closest escape we ever created," Kees said.

When they were all settled in the four protectors went on their way back to the farm. In the distance they saw a line of vehicle lights approaching on the road coming out of the city of Utrecht.

"I am going to drive my small herd of cows back and forth to the laborer's house," Johannes told the others. "It will wipe out the trail of our footsteps we created, just in case the Nazis spot it."

"Good idea Johannes."Levi remarked approvingly. Johannes returned an hour later, soaking wet from his nightly effort. It was just after twelve midnight when the sound of Pantzer vehicles rudely broke the peace in the village. They stopped in front of a farm. When the soldiers got out of the vehicles they entered the farmhouse. Minutes later the people who had been sleeping inside were forced out of the building. Some soldiers had been shooting in the air to enforce their demands. "Out, out of the house," they shouted, "We need this dwelling for our defense."

Within minutes the convoy of army vehicles had stopped at half a dozen farms and chased the inhabitants out of their homes. They all went somewhere in the darkness; to shacks and haystacks, stables and wherever they could find a roof for temporary cover from the elements. The Nazis did not make it to the farm where Kees, Levi and Robert were staying. That evening Kees and Levi thanked their God for His goodness and mercy.

Chapter Twelve

A RENEWED OCCUPATION

—∞—

The Generals in The Hague had not left on Frenzy Tuesday. Their orders had been to stay where they were until the Canadians had been defeated in Arnhem. The old occupying troops had left in panic. There were too many of them to try them for treason and the German command had chosen to let them go home. As they left they had ransacked the country of Holland by looting and stealing anything they could put their stealing claws on. T h e leadership, which had stayed put, had been promised by the high command in Berlin that fresh troops and equipment would arrive as soon as possible. It had taken two full weeks of chaos before the new troops had parachuted into Holland. The new equipment came a little later, which made the newly arrived troops nervous because they were not able to do their job properly by going on the streets in the cities of Holland.

The waiting time was spent training and educating the newly arrived troops about the stubborn behavior of the Dutch. That led to fanatics who would hurt many of the Resistance and people in hiding. The former rules were going to be enforced more aggresively. The distribution rules were going to be kept more precisely. The new troops had much more energy to keep order in this obstinate country.

That was their intention. Little did they know about the powerful underground or the deep-rooted enthusiasm for their freedom and the faith of the Calvinist nation. Lastly, the Dutch could not be suppressed because they loved their country and their Royal family.

When the long convoy of new equipment arrived, there were truckloads of motorcycles with sidecars, the favorite vehicle of the Nazis, hundreds of small trucks, large trucks, tanks and Pantzer vehicles brightly painted with Swastikas. The freshly shipped soldiers could not wait to get on the streets to start suppressing the people.

They had studied the way Razzias had been done and made them more thorough. During the first week of the new occupation thousands of hidden Jews had been found and shipped along with their hiders. Once more the concentration camps were filling up. The trains to the concentration camps were in use again. The cruelty of the new soldiers had no boundaries. They were determined to win the war, even though the Allied troops were in the neighboring countries and would soon begin liberating the Dutch.

Johanna and Cornelius had gone on the hunt for food again. The Nazi-employed clerk was being looked over by a freshly arrived soldier who did not have a clue that a lot of the food stamps were counterfeit. When the soldier asked for the food stamp for five pounds of potatoes, he took it in his hand and perused it carefully. Johanna knew that only that particular stamp was a real one. All the others they had accepted had been fake ones.

The soldier made a remark about the stamp to the clerk. "I think this stamp is counterfeit, look at this." He pointed at some stripes on the stamp which might have been caused by an ink stamp. Then the merchant, who had heard the comment of the soldier, came to look at it. Johanna knew he was not a collaborator with the enemy.

He took the stamp in his hand and said, "This stamp is as good as all the other ones; I know because I have seen this stamp thousands of times. Besides, I know this lady and I can vouch for her."

Johanna looked up into the eyes of the merchant and said, "Thank you Jan, I would not know the difference if I had a bad one." The statement was true. Johanna realized she had never been able to tell which ones were counterfeit. At that moment she determined in her heart that she would avoid this location for the sake of the merchant. He had backed her up, but what if the soldier really stumbled onto a fake stamp. They would arrest the merchant, maybe even torture him and throw him in jail.

The daily life for the Dutch became much more difficult with the newly-arrived fanatics. They were out to arrest anyone who committed even the least infraction against the Nazi rules. Johanna and Cornelius walked the two miles home with their treasure of food. Suddenly, out of an alley they had just passed a man in rags ran towards them and tore the bag of potatoes out of Johanna's hands. He turned back the way he had come and disappeared into the alley.

Cornelius ran after him to see which door he entered into, but when he had turned the corner the man was gone.

Angry, the little boy came running towards his mom and said, "Now what, Mom? Now we have no potatoes for all of us." He had carefully avoided saying "for us and our friends."

Johanna's answer calmed him down, "This man probably has a family which is hungry, too. Perhaps they need the potatoes more than we do?"

"But, mom, we need them, we are hungry".

"Yes I agree, but we have some other food yet and you have your garden too. I am sure you will be able to get us all some cabbage?"

"I can, yes, I can!" he shouted. "I would never steal from a mother and her child."

"I know you would not and that makes you the better person. Tonight we shall pray for this man and his family, all right?"

"I sure hope daddy is coming home tonight because he will go and find this man and tell him to come and ask us for food; and if he does my daddy would give it to him." Those were the last words of the conversation.

Desperation was beginning to make animals of people and the Nazis created that kind of atmosphere. Were there families like that in Germany too? How much more dreadful was it to be hungry in the land where all this misery came from?

Johanna wiped a tear from her face and said a short prayer. "Lord protect the mothers and children in Germany too. If they are hungry, provide them with food. If they are cold, provide them with warmth and if they are lonely, give them Your comfort. In the name of Jesus, amen."

They came home to see that the street had been barricaded and hundreds of soldiers were banging on the doors, demanding them to be opened. When Johanna and Cornelius saw the scene unfolding before their eyes, her first reaction was to turn around.

She hesitated for a moment and then decided she would go home and face the house search, rather than letting the soldiers break open her door and ransack the house to find nothing. Johanna had to go through the barricade in order to get to her front door where soldiers were banging on it. She approached the soldier at the opening in the barricade and pointed at her house.

"I need to go to my house there and open it with my key before they break the door down."

The soldier yelled at his colleagues who had been banging at her door. They stopped their banging and turned around.

Johanna yelled to them, "I am here and I will open the door in a minute."

She hoped the guests under the floor had taken their measures and moved into the concrete bunker underneath the staircase. After the usual, "Ausweiss bitte," and a thorough look at her ID she was allowed to walk to her house with Cornelius and she opened the door for the impatient Nazis.

These Nazis very meticulously searched the house. The usual *discovery* was met with great enthusiasm as they moved the table and the carpet in the front room. She heard one of the soldiers triumphantly shout, "We found it! That's where they're hiding!"

Quickly four soldiers held their guns pointed at the hatch that had come into sight after the carpet had been removed. A fifth soldier was prying the hatch open with his bayonet. The hatch popped upwards and four guns immediately were ready to shoot into the hatch.

Fools, Johanna thought, *they think we are stupid enough to hide people that way*. Before they could contain themselves to first look inside the hatch, their guns went off. The loud bang could be heard throughout the street. Other soldiers came rushing over to join in the excitement of catching fugitive *Jude* (Jews).

Nothing but a cloud of dust came out of the hole beneath the hatch. It took a whole five minutes before the excited Nazis could see what was beneath the cloud of dust they had created. Finally one of them looked. He saw a square concrete box with nothing in it. He bent down and felt around the concrete to see if there was an opening or a secret handle he could turn. There was nothing.

The sergeant in charge looked at Johanna and asked, "What is that for?"

"It is just a safe keeping box in which people kept their valuables and papers. We don't have any of that, so there is nothing in it."

The sergeant gave a command. They all left disappointed but ready for the next adventure. Hunting down people was the favorite work of these newly-arrived soldiers. They had no idea how inventive the Dutch were. They would soon find out.

"Cornelius, go step on the crack board so our friends can go back to their normal place. After that, would you look into the garden and see if there are any potatoes left?"

The morning was peaceful, the sun was shining brightly, and the farmer and his wife had already milked their six cows, which was all they had left from a herd of sixty.

Anna was busy making breakfast when the three visitors walked into the large kitchen. Then all of a sudden, the ground began to tremble. The sound of what seemed to be a thousand trucks could be heard from the road in front of the farm. The driveway to the farm was only fifty meters long, which was very short for a farm's location. A minute later a convoy of trucks, tanks, Pantzer trucks and personnel vehicles, blowing up large clouds of dust, were humming past in what seemed an endless lineup.

They were on their way to the big cities in the West of the country, The Hague, Rotterdam and Amsterdam. They were replacing the old and obsolete vehicles that had fled the country with all the stolen cargo. This was the new equipment that the Nazis expected to win the war with.

The spectators looked at the endless convoy and thought what a waste of money and time the Nazis were making. Were they that stupid, to think they could win an unjust war against so many Allies that had already landed in Normandy and had taken back a third of Europe?

The soldiers inside the trucks, the armored vehicles, the Pantzer trucks and on the motor cycles had been worked up into a frenzy; a passion for the Fuehrer. They had been brainwashed into thinking that, if they would annihilate all the Jews in Europe, they would become the world rulers.

This particular draft of the Nazi army was young and inexperienced. From fifteen to seventeen years of age, they had been drafted only six months before and had their training for only a few months. They had been indoctrinated to believe that the peace of the world depended on them; if they would only do what the Fuehrer expected of them.

Breakfast only consisted of a large bowl of oats, because there was no bread available at all. The day before, a German truck had come to the village and stopped in front of the only bakery in town. With guns in their hands the Nazis had entered the bakery and demanded everything in the store and in the bakery behind the store to be loaded into their truck.

"We need it for The Reich," they had said.

The baker had retorted, "We need it for the citizens of the village." It was too much to say to a freshly recruited army sergeant. He slapped the baker in the face with the butt of his riffle. Blood gushed out of the baker's face as he fell to the floor. Several neighbors saw what happened. They had been waiting for bread and then the Nazis took it all. They saw it, but they did not dare to intervene. They knew it could mean certain death for any one of them.

Kees put his thought to words after he had swallowed his oats. "If we get out of here quickly and follow the convoy of Nazi vehicles, we should be able to get home pretty quickly. It would seem natural that an ambulance would follow a convoy of army vehicles. We could only hope that there won't be any accidents or we're not expected to take care of wounded people as ambulance personnel normally do."

They agreed that it was a good idea but that they should stay at least five kilometers behind the convoy so they would have an escape option open; just in case something should occur that they had no control over. That part of their trip home had been the easiest part. Then they reached the town of Bodegraven.

Chapter Thirteen

ATTACK FROM THE RESISTANCE

The meadows and fields on both sides of the Old Rijn were still green and beautiful. Where at one time thousands of cows had been grazing and making the fields look like a Van Gogh painting, the farmers had tried to keep other smaller animals like goats and sheep in the fields. Too soon, the Nazis had realized that they could have a new source of food. Within one year the Nazis had taken the small animals away. Now the fields were waiting for a different flock; one which would liberate them from the yoke of the Nazis. They will come, they are saying to each other, and one day the Allies will fill our fields and drive the Nazis out of our country, just like the Nazis had driven their flocks and herds away.

The strong belief, which the good and religious Dutch had kept going, made them even stronger knowing that no foreign rulers or dictators could ever bridle their freedom. The number of members of the Resistance had grown to maximum capacity. Every man over 16 years of age who had not been taken by the Nazis for various reasons, mainly because they were farmers and farmhands who were needed to supply the Nazis with food, had joined the Resistance. But there were also men who had come from the cities and had gone underground in the country. They were the fighters for the Resistance, the underground army of Holland.

The day and night before the convoy of vehicles with the soldiers was scheduled to pass through the town of Bodegraven they had all gathered at the local fire station. They had come in droves in the middle of the night. There were no Germans in town since they had fled to their home country just two weeks before and the NSB-ers had fled with their taskmasters.

They all knew that a new army of Nazis was on its way and they were going to do everything to stop their progress. The meeting at the fire station had lasted two full hours. They had reached the point of no return and then they all went back home to sleep that early morning at the end of September 1944.

There was a stretch of road just past the town where there had once been a flour mill. Not a regular antique windmill but a modern steam-driven mill. The farmers used to be able to go to the mill with sacks of grain and wait for the miller to grind them into flour. This particular flour was used as food for their pigs. Together with the whey, the remnant of what was left over from making butter and cheese, the flour was made into a wash that the pigs would noisily lap up in minutes.

It was that spot on that stretch of road that was chosen for the attack. The tall miller's tower offered a great view and would be set up with two machine guns the Resistance had stolen from the departing Nazis just two weeks before. On one side of the road was the river. On the opposite side of the river was a long row of knotty willows. The attackers had perfect cover and any one of the Nazis who would be driven into the river would be shot from that side. The plan was good, but was the Resistance strong enough against a trained and well-equipped Nazi force?

They had counted one hundred and twenty men for the attacking force. Not all had guns, but they had hand grenades. They had spent the next day preparing for the attack. A handful of them had made bent nails and forged two of them together so they would stand up on the pavement. They had filled potato bags with sand and had brought them to the site of the attack. Not one of them could sleep that night. Never before had they made such an elaborate plan of attack.

Kees and his friends in the ambulance were keeping a distance of two kilometers from the convoy of Nazi vehicles. Most of the time they could see the dust cloud in front of them. Often they could see the entire length of the convoy when there was a turn in the road. "There must be more than a hundred vehicles there. I hope there are not too many soldiers inside them. I heard from a man whom I had spoken to when we had to wait yesterday, that thousands of troops had parachuted into the West. There were more Nazis than ever before who had dropped out of the sky just a few days ago. The vehicles in front of us are to equip them," Kees told his friends.

They approached the town of Bodegraven. It was a small town of no more than five thousand inhabitants. All of a sudden they saw the distance between the convoy and the ambulance had grown shorter. “Let’s slow down or stop to make sure we keep our distance. But keep an eye on them at all times.” Levi warned.

They turned into the driveway of a large villa at the outskirts of the town. Within minutes a lady knocked on the window and in broken German she tried to explain that they had to leave. When she had finished speaking she lifted her fist at them and uttered some words Kees chose not to hear.

He opened the door and stepped out of the cabin. “My dear lady,” he began speaking in perfect Dutch of course, “We are not Germans even though we look like it. We are all Dutch from the Resistance in The Hague. We are on our way home from a mission in Arnhem to find out what was going on there and if we could expect our liberation soon. It turned out quite different, didn’t it?”

At first he could see that the lady was skeptical, but when he mentioned the Resistance, her eyes lit up and she accepted the words Kees had spoken. Instead of chasing them away she gestured to the driver to follow her to the barn. She opened the wide door and urged him to drive the ambulance inside.

“Come inside, all of you,” she urged. “Quickly, I have to tell you something very important.” She went before them into the villa.

But before they entered Kees said, “We have to keep an eye on the convoy. We have been traveling safely behind them since Utrecht.”

“Not for long you won’t, my friends” the lady said as she turned towards them. “Within minutes there will be a huge attack on that convoy. We have an army of Resistance men all staged on the roadside outside of the town. They are armed to the teeth. We have machine guns in place and I will be surprised if there will be one vehicle left without a flat tire, let alone an alive soul.”

The three visitors smiled in a grim way and Levi asked,” Have they fought against a Nazi army before? Are they trained soldiers?”

The lady shook her head. “No, but they are motivated, stubborn Dutch farmers, and the ambush is well prepared.”

Kees shook his head, but he remained silent. What could he say? That they were all going to die? Those brave men who did not really know what they could expect, would they all have to die?

At that moment they heard the sound of gunfire. The noise grew quickly from a huge amount of explosions. Then they heard the staccato noise of machine guns, exploding grenades and screams of wounded people. For a moment it was silent, they could hear the screeching sound of tanks that were turning into position.

The shots from the tank cannons sounded like bombs that had been dropped from planes. Big explosions followed. From where they were they could see flames going up high into the sky. More explosions followed. For at least an hour the shooting went on.

The sky was now turning black with the smoke of burning rubber and gasoline. The tumult finally stopped; just an occasional rifle shot was heard. No one in the town dared to go look at the certain devastation. Finally they heard the sound of army boots marching towards the town. Kees listened intently. It was hard to tell how many men were coming towards them. He ran outside and quickly closed the doors of the barn.

When he came back inside he asked the lady, "Is there a place for us to hide around here? Quickly please, we need to get out of here. The Nazis are known to pick the biggest houses for their temporary quarters. Who knows if it is going to be this house."

Levi, who had just been racking his mind about what they could do in this predicament, asked the lady, "Is there a door big enough for our ambulance to exit on the other side of your barn?" He knew it was a customary thing and often there was a river behind the barn.

The lady nodded, "Yes there is, and there is a pathway which goes into an orchard which ends about a mile from here at a narrow road."

"We have no time to lose." Kees yelled, "Run, come on, let's go!" They all followed Kees who had spotted a side door in the barn. Robert jumped behind the wheel and Levi opened the back doors of the barn.

The ambulance rolled out of the barn slowly. Robert did not start the engine to avoid any excessive noise. The vehicle rolled down into the cherry orchard and within minutes it was out of sight of the villa.

Many brave Resistance fighters died that day; most of the rest of them were wounded. The wounded ones had looked at the devastation they had made. They asked themselves, was it worth it? Not one vehicle was intact, except for the five tanks and five of the Pantzer vehicles. There was nothing but a big heap of useless steel. Two hundred and ten soldiers, a few petty officers and one Major marched into the town of Bodegraven. Of the fallen Nazis, there was no known count. According to the survivors there must have been at least one hundred and fifty dead Nazis in the attack. Most of them had been the drivers of the vehicles.

Luckily the Nazis took possession of the local school instead of seizing the homes. The Major in charge had sent a motorcyclist to The Hague to find out what he should do. Doctors in town had to be found to take care of the wounded soldiers. The thought of repercussions against the citizens of Bodegraven had not occurred yet to the inexperienced Major, until the motorcyclist came back the next morning followed by a dozen Gestapo Officers. Two days later the town had to pay the price for the attack. Twenty men had been rounded up. Without any form of justice they were brought in front of a firing squad.

The ambulance with Kees, Levi and Robert had dropped off the lady who had saved them from the Nazis and the ensuing battle. She was dropped off at her family's home in Alphen. From there they had been able to take a major road to The Hague. The three came home just after the largest and meanest Razzia that had ever been held in the neighborhood. All three men were extremely exhausted from what was meant to be a quick trip to the frontlines. It had taken them eight days total. The events had taken their toll on the brave Resistance men. It would take weeks for them to recover from all the death and destruction they had seen firsthand all over their beloved country.

A new war, inside World War II, had begun. It would turn out to be the worst of the five years the war had lasted in the country. It would result in many more Jews to be found and hundreds of Resistance members to be found out and executed.

Chapter Fourteen

SUBTLE RESISTANCE

Being back at home was a blessing for a time. After Kees had taken three days of rest at home and played with Cornelius who had to show him the growth of his big white rabbit and his garden, which was still yielding crops of vegetables; he began to feel guilty to be just sitting at home and doing nothing.

It was time to get back to "work", if you could call it that. The factory where Kees had worked before had been closed down after Frenzy Tuesday had come. The soldiers who had suppressed the citizens by making them do slave labor had fled to Germany and the NSB-ers had taken the hint. Some of them had gone with the Nazis, others had gone underground in their own country in fear they would be arrested by their countrymen.

The first thing Kees did was to visit his friend Frans. He needed to know what his fellow Resistance members had learned and what was happening in The Hague with all the new troops coming in and he also wanted to tell them about the attack on the convoy in Bodegraven.

"A lot has changed in the last week," were the first words that came out of Frans' mouth after their greeting. The two had gone through so much that nothing surprised them anymore. "This new draft of Nazis are meaner and dumber, they have virtually no experience but they do everything by the book you know, 'Befehl ist Befehl'. They have held Razzias more thoroughly and found a lot of hiding places, plus they arrested many Jews at places where the hiders had slacked in security since Frenzy Tuesday. The leadership wants to have everyone do more subtle kinds of acts of resistance. The motto is, destroy their equipment and they have no means to suppress us."

Kees was listening intensively, "I have seen how stupid the Nazis were when we were behind the convoy that was attacked in Bodegraven; they took no security measures at all and ran into the biggest ambush they had ever experienced. Unfortunately the Gestapo came to their rescue and made the population suffer. Twenty men were shot; they had been picked at random."

Frans took a small jelly jar in his hand and showed it to Kees. "This is our newest weapon. This little jar has the capability of blowing up ten vehicles."

Kees took it in his hand and looked at the little jar in disbelief, "How?" In the jar were small pieces of phosphor in water.

"As soon as these chunks come out of the water and are placed on the road, they get stuck in the tread of the tires of the army vehicles. Some kilometers down the road, the chunks of phosphor cause the tires to burst into flames and moments later the entire truck blows up."

"Wow," said Kees, "but what about any private vehicles?"

"There are none any more. All the cars have been seized and only German vehicles are allowed on the roads."

"Tomorrow night we are all going out to spread the phosphor throughout the entire city. By the way, the curfew is still there but the Nazis are no longer enforcing it because they are afraid to go outside their compounds at night. Still we need to be careful and do our jobs in a subtle way. Tomorrow all of us are going to warn all the citizens to stay at home as much as possible the next day because there will be many explosions in the city."

"We will teach the Nazis a lesson which will even make them scared to go outside during the day time. There will be nothing they can do about it, the only thing they might do is, arrest some people and shoot them as an example. We have been worried about that, but if we let them do their normal dirty work, many more will be killed. It has been a grave decision, but when was war ever humane?"

Many subtle actions were being prepared and implemented by the Resistance. A country-wide action was mobilized to scare the new Nazis out of their wits and it was working. The Resistance had become the example for the citizens, which gave them hope in hopeless situations. Another action was directed at the railroads. If the trains could not run anymore they could not transport large groups of people to the concentration camps.

An attack was prepared at the central supplies warehouse of the rail company. All the remaining uniforms were stolen and handed out to Resistance people. Clad in those uniforms they went all over the country to unscrew the bolts which held the rail in place. Within weeks hundreds of trains derailed and the train traffic had come to a complete halt. The Nazis did not have the equipment in place to repair the rails and to remove the derailed wagons. The Nazis did not know who had done the sabotage and no one could pinpoint who was behind the country-wide activities.

The car of S.S. General Rauter, burned by chunks of phosphor.

Unfortunately, any Resistance member who was caught in those days was punished immediately. It was clear that the Resistance had become very effective and that the citizens had begun to look up to the underground organization. Most of the NSB-ers felt the pressure and stopped doing their dirty treasonous activities. The tables had been turned on them; any NSB-er who got caught was put away somewhere to wait out his pending trial after the liberation.

Several abandoned buildings, particularly old factories on the outskirts of cities where the Nazis did not dare to come, were made into temporary prisons for the NSB-ers. The biggest problem was how to feed the traitors. Food had become so scarce that even the Nazi soldiers were hungry. The NSB-er prisons were often the last place where people would want to use up their meager food supply.

All the food suppliers were controlled by the Nazis; a special department of the Gestapo kept charge of the food factories and the farms. An elaborate distribution stamp system was in place but it failed miserably. The abundance of counterfeit distribution stamps, which was continually printed, messed up the distribution system. The population in general was hungry and the weather was getting colder. A very difficult time was ahead for the Dutch citizens, but the constant news on the movements of the Allied Forces kept them going.

The Americans are coming!

The Dutch radio station which was broadcasting from England on the BBC was supplying news of the progress of the liberators. *Radio Oranje* was on the air twelve hours every day. Instructions for the Resistance were wrapped into stories and Bible texts. For those who needed to hear the message, it was loud and clear. For the hopeless Nazi operators, it was a constant frustration.

Openly the radio station was announcing information about the fate of the Jews in the concentration camps. Even some Nazi soldiers could not believe the news. Many Dutch citizens did not want to believe the stories about the mass murdering that was going on in the concentration camps. The Jews, all fifty thousand of them who were still in hiding, heard the news too. They became more grateful to their hosts and more thankful for the little food they were receiving. Better hungry and safe and alive, than dead and buried, they would say when the host would apologize for the meager food they were able to give them.

A new and serious problem was showing up in the country. The Nazis had sabotaged and blown up several water treatment plants and the regular supply of water had stopped. In the cities it was a huge problem. Some people had to walk for miles to find a bucket of decent fresh water, which, when brought home, would have to be boiled to become drinkable.

Cornelius had his special chores to do; one of them was to get hot water from the Waterbaas, two streets down from the Deiman Straat. The water was boiled in a huge tank using anything which would burn. All the neighbors would get hot water for their laundry, baths, and showers. The regular bath house did not work. It was closed. The water from the Waterbaas was not drinkable or potable water. It was taken from the river nearby and it was very unsanitary.

Every Monday morning Johanna was doing her laundry. Three times that day, Cornelius had to walk to the Waterbaas and carry a heavy steel bucket full of hot water over a distance of three hundred meters to his mother. He had to pay the thirty cents for each bucket of water. On Fridays it was bathing time at the van Rijn residence.

Cornelius had to walk the same distance six times that day. First for the Jewish people, who one by one were coming upstairs into the kitchen where they would stand in a large galvanized steel tub. The remaining water was dumped out in the street. At one time Johanna had told him to use the water for the plants in his back yard. Cornelius had said, “Mom, this is dirty water, so it will make dirty vegetables."

Johanna had laughed at his remark and told him, "You better ask Marie at the farm about that, because I think it will make no difference."

The next time he visited the Brandwijk Farm he did ask Marie, "My mom said I should give the dirty bathwater to my plants in the garden, do you think that is good?"

Marie had laughed just like his mom, "Absolutely not, Cornelius. The bathwater contains soaps and they will kill your vegetable plants."

"I am glad that I refused it," he said wisely. "Mothers don't know everything and especially mothers from the city."

Often when he carried a full water bucket he was laughed at by the boys in the street, "Are you finally going to wash yourself?" they would yell at him. Cornelius did not care. *They don't know what we are doing for all our friends down below the house.* But after the war he was going to tell them and then he would be able to tell them how selfish they and their families had been during the war.

Cornelius loved to go down to the friends beneath the house. To him it was fun to sit in the sand and talk to the Jewish people. He had seen so many different people in their hiding place. His first goal, every time new people had come, was to remember their names. He always brought a piece of paper and a pencil with him so he could write down their names. They were interesting names and often difficult to spell.

He had spent days learning how to write and spell words. The schools had been closed for a long time, but Johanna had enjoyed teaching her little one to write. When he goes to school after the war he will be the only one in the class who can write. His writing went very slowly. Letter by letter he asked the Jewish friend to spell out his or her name. Then he would ask for help to pronounce the name correctly. His final question was always, "What does your name mean?" He made a point of remembering the meaning, often rehearsing both the spelling and the meanings.

Before he went down below, he would study his little notes and made it a point to remember each name, and each meaning. The next time he went down he would take his inquiry a little further. His question to each of the Jews was, "Where does your family come from originally?" That question brought up some very interesting stories which he loved to hear and he never forgot them.

Chapter Fifteen

A WOMAN WITHOUT A STAR

Kees had promised to visit the sister of Krelis, the farmer in Oosterbeek. He had also promised to visit the sister of Arie the Jew without a Star. After having rested from the exhausting trip, and having met with the local Resistance, he prepared to make the two visits. For Krelis' sister he had brought some food in the form of cheese, butter and a bag of potatoes.

She used to live in the Java Straat which was a bike ride of half an hour, going through the bombed center of The Hague. He decided to take Cornelius with him to carry the new ID's for the sister and for the Jewish girl.

It always took him two times to provide a person with a new Ausweiss. The first trip he had to make was because he had to get the particulars of the person and take a picture; then he had to go back to the printer to put it all together in order to deliver the completed product. The old square box camera was hidden in a lunch box with a double bottom. The Nazis would wonder why he was carrying a camera with him and, if confiscated, it could cause a lot of trouble.

Kees was warned that the new Nazi force was much more thorough and that he could expect several searches; the first of which came at the tunnel under the train station in The Hague. There was just one way through it and right before the tunnel they had set up a heavily armed blockade.

While Cornelius kept sitting on top of the food supplies for the farmer's sister, the soldiers frisked Kees thoroughly. Meanwhile Cornelius was waiting for the possible sign from his dad, in case he had to start crying. The soldiers looked at the skinny little guy on the bicycle and shook their heads. No contraband there; but they were looking at the bicycle, that was a sturdy one they could use.

One of the soldiers began to walk towards the bicycle when Kees gave the sign. The crying stopped the soldier in his tracks. Would he do that to a child? Let the boy go walking? He thought of his own children back in Germany and decided to leave the bike and the boy alone. Another soldier who had followed him asked him what he wanted to do and with a somber voice he said: "Lass mahl gehen. The children don't need to suffer."

Once more they had escaped a possible death sentence if the soldiers would have found the fake ID's Cornelius had hidden on his body. The ride continued, and when they passed the Zoo they were confronted with an even larger barricade. The Nazis had seized the large dome which was once the prize exhibit of the Zoo. Now it had become a different kind of zoo, this time it had human predators occupying the beautiful dome.

All people who passed by the Zoo were searched, their Ausweiss was questioned and compared to samples of falsifications. An armored transport truck was ready to load up any one who had a wrong ID. The ID Kees produced was real and he had no trouble going through. It was Cornelius he was worried about. Should he continue to expose the little guy to the huge risk of being detected? Kees decided to pray about it and to talk to Frans to see if there was another way to transport the contraband papers.

After a long wait they were on their way once more. The Java Straat was only half a mile further down the road and the address had been easy to find the first time. Not so this time. A bomb had hit the very building the sister had lived in. Kees hoped she survived the explosion and began to inquire at the severely damaged neighboring buildings. He was lucky; the first doorbell he rang was answered by an old lady who had known Ina van Houten, Krelis' sister. She now lives on the other side of the street above the book store she pointed out. He crossed the road and entered the book store the lady had indicated. Kees recognized her when he had come inside. She, in turn, did not recognize the father and son who had come into the store.

"Good morning, sir," she said in a friendly tone, "What can I do for you today?" Then she noticed something familiar in the two and said: "I know you sir, where have I seen you before?" All Kees said was: "Your brother Krelis." "Yes, now I see, would you come this way to our little office please?" She held a finger to her lips indicating not to talk. When they were in the little office she closed the door and let out a deep sigh, "We have a few Nazis in the store and I did not want anybody to hear what you were going to say, as you can well understand".

She walked towards Kees and gave him a hug, "I have so much to tell you, but I have to tend the store as well, can you stay a while until the owners come back? Then we can go upstairs to my apartment and chat."

Kees nodded, "Yes, I could, but how long is a while?"

"About an hour," she answered.

Kees shook his head, "That would be a long time to waste. I tell you what, I have another visit to make here in the Celebes Straat, and we will come back after that, okay?"

Before they left, Kees thought of something, "Can I leave the things I brought from Krelis with you now? I don't want to risk keeping them with me. The Nazis are getting so nasty in their searches."

She agreed, "Here is the key to my apartment, just leave it inside the hallway."

Kees was relieved to unload his precious cargo. Never before had it bothered him to have contraband food or papers on him. Was he getting afraid of the Nazis? He decided to pray about that too.

No more risk! Don't take any more risk, a voice was repeating it in his mind, sounding louder and louder; yet he went on to the Celebes Straat to visit a Jewish girl. He did not notice the man standing across the street. He did not see the Nazi motorcycle on the corner when he rang the doorbell of the Celebes Straat number 128. The door opened when its lock was released by a rope which was pulled from upstairs. Together with Cornelius, he climbed the steep staircase. He had parked the bicycle in the narrow hallway. After he had closed the door, he did not see the man across the street come closer to the house. He also did not hear the motorcycle come up to the front door.

Something inside of him kept urging him to be careful, was it too late? The girl upstairs greeted him with joy. "Kees, how nice of you to come and see me, it has been a long time. What have you been up to?" Suddenly, Kees had to listen to his inner voice and walked to the window. Carefully he stood away from it and hid behind the long blue velvet curtains; he slipped the thin white lacey material aside and looked down at the street. The man he had not seen was talking with two soldiers on their motorcycles in front of the house. Kees wondered where they had come from, and finally he understood what the voice within him had said, "Don't take a risk!"

Kees took immediate action. Ilse Heyermans, the girl he was visiting was in grave danger. He softly called out her name and she came over to him, also peeking through the curtains. "Have you seen them before, Ilse?"

She shook her head, "But there was a man who has been standing around here for the last two days."

"Did he see you in person? In other words did you go outside at all?"

"No I did not, in fact I have not been outside for a week."

"They must be waiting for you, as soon as you walk out the door, they will arrest you; believe me I have seen this scene many times before. We better find a way to get you out of here. Even more so, now that they know you have Cornelius and me as visitors." Kees looked around the apartment: "Is there any way out of here?"

Cornelius had been looking and said: "There is a balcony in the back." Kees went to look at it. There was a patio down below and a wooden fence which surrounded it; behind the fence was an alley. It was a four meter drop to the patio and there was nothing to climb down on.

"Sheets! Do you have three sheets, Ilse?" he asked. She did and brought them to him a minute later. Kees tied them together and tied one end to the railing of the balcony. "Ilse, I am going to let you go down. Do you see the gate there in the fence? I think it is unlocked, at least I don't see a lock on it. When you are down, go see if you can get out, if so, raise your thumb to me, don't yell or talk, everything needs to be done in total silence.

"When you are in the alley take a left and go to the Java Straat; do you know the book store there?" She nodded. "Go to the store but don't go inside. Next to the store is a door to the apartment above. Here is the key to the apartment. Go inside and wait there. We'll come as soon as the coast is clear. The Nazis probably will ask me a lot of questions; but I think I can handle it.

"They might want to search your apartment. I'll let them have their way. I'll just tell them that you must be out shopping and you might be back later." Minutes later when they saw her walk away through the alley. Kees raised the string of sheets, took the knots out and folded them away into the closet. "Now comes the tricky part," he said to Cornelius. "We go out the front door and act as if nothing happened. They will probably ask what I was doing there. I will just tell them something. Let's go, and remember, you may have to do the crying act. Make it a spectacular one," he said with a smile.

It went exactly like he had expected, the Gestapo officer in civilian clothing stopped him the minute he pulled the door shut and commanded, "Halt, Ausweiss bitte." Kees was putting Cornelius in his seat and pulled out his ID and a letter from the Symowitz Factory which said that he was allowed to visit women who were living alone and help them with little tasks in their homes.

The interrogator asked Kees if he knew the girl who was living there. "I just know she needed some help with her sink which was leaking. I just help where I can. I don't mingle in peoples' personal affairs. I fixed it and left; she was not at home. What else can I say?"

The Gestapo man did not take his explanation that easy, "How did you get in if she was not at home?" he demanded.

"Oh, that is very easy, let me show you." Kees stepped towards the door and stuck his hand into the letter box flap which was in the middle of the door. He pulled the string and the door opened. "You see, it is that easy."

They went upstairs, the two soldiers and the Gestapo man. He had pushed Kees in front of him and they left Cornelius on the street. Instantly he began to cry and kept crying until Kees was sent down to 'comfort' him.

It took the three men only five minutes to make a mess of the apartment and to determine that no one was home. "You can go, but you don't need to come back here. She will be gone forever." The Gestapo officer said in a menacing voice.

"Thank you, Lord," Kees said under his breath, "That is another one we get to walk away from without any trouble." When he mounted his bike he turned in the opposite direction he had to take to the bookstore in the Java Straat.

They rode around the area for fifteen minutes before returning to the Java Straat. Kees walked into the book store where for the second time a group of Nazi soldiers was browsing. Apparently the owners had returned and when they saw Kees entering the store they pointed to the upstairs without saying a word. Kees left quickly and rang the doorbell of the apartment. In an instant the door opened and there was Ilse. She had been waiting in the little vestibule and Ina had not even noticed her.

"Let's go upstairs and I will introduce you to your newest friend and traveling companion. You are going to move to Arnhem next week where you will be reunited with your brother who has been defeating the Nazis just like you; without a Star." Ina van Houten heard the footsteps on her wooden stair case and had come to the landing. "Well what do you know? You brought a friend, I cannot wait to meet her," Ina said in a friendly voice. Cornelius could not wait to tell about the adventure they had just had by making the lady slide down a rolled up sheet and escape from the Gestapo. He told them about the search the Nazis had done of Ilse's apartment and how they had messed up everything.

Kees gave Ilse a warning, "You can never go back to your apartment, do you hear? Never! The Nazis are expecting you back any time and they'll be waiting for you. They have a one-way ticket for you to Westerbork and from there to heaven." He addressed Ina: "Can she stay here for a couple of days?"

And looking Ilse in the eye he asked, "Will you promise me to stay inside here all the time and not even look out the windows?"

She answered "Ja," but Kees had a feeling she was not taking the situation serious enough.

"You have to understand and realize that if the Nazis catch you, you will die. I am here to protect you and bring you to a safe place where you can stay together with your brother."

The two young ladies who had met each other just minutes ago looked at each other. They were different in appearance, but Kees had said they would have to be sisters in order to get out of here safely. A Dutch blond and a black haired Jewish girl had to look like sisters? "How do you suppose we do that?" Ina had asked Kees.

"Peroxide from the drug store, scissors and some makeup. I will be back tomorrow with my camera and I will tell you how you will have to prepare to leave."

Cornelius had listened to the conversation and looked at the Jewish girl thinking, she wouldn't be as pretty after she messes up her beautiful black curls. They left for a bike ride through several road blocks. This time they had nothing to hide, yet the Nazis had been nasty at each barricade.

At home there was another problem. Johanna was in tears when Kees walked into his house. "Daniel, the oldest of the friends downstairs is very ill we need to get a doctor to come as soon as possible. Can you go to Dr. Kalis and have him come here? You know he is the only doctor who we can trust. I only hope that the Nazis don't follow him and check out where he goes. We'll have to have a back-up plan just in case. What do you suggest, Kees?"

He thought for a minute, and then he answered his wife, "Our little actor will have to be on standby for this one. Here is my plan: we will bring Daniel upstairs so the doctor does not have to go down below, but not until the coast is clear in case the Nazis come. The moment they come into the house, Cornelius has to be in his bed and play to be very sick. Ten minutes after the Nazis leave, we'll have Daniel come upstairs for the doctor."

Everything had to be staged to deceive the Gestapo intruders; nothing in everyday life could be taken for granted. Kees left to notify the doctor and Johanna prepared Cornelius for his temporary sickbed.

Kees had to make two visits. The first was to the doctor. Dr.Kalis was a jovial man and he was very loyal to the Resistance. Kees had needed his assistance on many occasions. Each time he had to brief the doctor of the plan they would prepare for his coming.

"Yes, the Nazis often follow me and unfortunately if the people who are having guests are not careful enough it can cause a lot of trouble. Just last week two Jewish people had been arrested at a house I went to and it was not even for the Jewish people that I had made the visit. When I arrived at the house the wife was ill and the husband had let me inside. Within minutes the Gestapo came and did an entire search of the house. They had the two Jews in a shack in their back yard and the Nazis had never searched there before. This time they did, and they arrested all four of them, the two Jews and the hiders. They are supposed to be still in jail awaiting their sentence and you know what that means."

"Poor people," Kees remarked, "the Nazis have been getting really thorough lately."

Kees informed the doctor how he would stage the situation. "We have our son in bed, playing sick. We will wait for the Nazis to come, if they do. After their inevitable visit, we will bring our Jewish guest upstairs for you to examine him. That way the Nazis will be gone when you get to see him. The Nazis will only be there for a minute or two."

"Well, sometimes they will make a total search of your house and give you a hard time," the doctor warned.

"We will be ready for them. They have never had any luck in our house, but then again these are fresh Nazis and they don't know with whom they are dealing." Kees answered with a smile. "I agree, but we'll be careful anyway."

His next visit was to the printer down below the ruins of the school. Kees had to be very careful entering the ruins and went to the building through several back alleys. At the same time he watched to see if he was being followed or not.

No one had ever found the print shop; even children who had been playing at the ruined school building had never found the entrance to the printer's home and workshop. He walked the long hallway in the former basement of the school and came to the underground print shop.

The printer had heard him coming. Whenever someone lifts the fallen door and drops it he could hear the sound and would know that someone in the know was on his way. The two Resistance workers did not waste any time. "I need ID's, for two young ladies who are going to be transported tomorrow,. Can you do that?" Kees asked.

"What names and addresses do you want on them?"

"Ina and Ilse Jansen, two sisters from now on," Kees answered. "Can you have them ready by say, tonight?" The printer nodded. Within minutes Kees was back on his bicycle and hurried home. *I better be there when the doctor comes so I can take care of the Gestapo if they decide to have a house search,* he thought to himself.

No one's home was sacred to the Nazis. No one's life was private in the latter days of the war. Within minutes of the doctor's arrival the Gestapo was there, too. Their loud knocking on the door triggered a chain of events inside the house which had become almost a daily routine.

It was all staged when the five soldiers rushed inside and accosted the doctor. "What are you doing here, Herr Doctor?" The Gestapo Sergeant asked. "Who is sick here in this house?" Johanna pointed at the bed room where Cornelius was lying in his bed. His face was grey from the charcoal Johanna had rubbed on his face. He did look very sick, the Germans could see that, and as they backed away from him they heard the Sergeant say, "Do a complete search of this house, Schnell."

The usual scene followed: Removing the table and the carpet and the triumphant exhilaration, when they had found the cutout of the hatch. One of them pried it open and guns were pointed at the opening. Three shots sounded and dust filled the room for the umpteenth time.

Kees was grateful that he did not have any fake food stamps or ID's in the house. The thoroughness in which the Nazis searchers went through his house would have brought anything illegal (in the Nazi's eyes) to the surface. They shot with their guns through the walls and the floors and listened for possible outcries from hidden people. Their efforts were all in vain and a frustrated Nazi sergeant gave order to depart.

Doctor Kalis had taken a seat on the bed where Cornelius was lying. When the door had shut behind the Nazi intruders he asked for the real patient to be brought to him. Johanna shook her head and said, "Please sir, have patience, we have experienced that the Nazis will pretend to have gone and then after five minutes they barge in again. They have had astonishing results with that method."

She was right. Five minutes later they heard a bang on the door again and voices shouted, "Aufmachen schnell." Johanna looked at the doctor and simply nodded her head. They opened the door as quickly as they could get to it and the same group of soldiers ran through the house to see if anything had been changed or moved. "Leider Nieghts," they heard one of the soldiers say as they left as quickly as they had barged in.

"We still have to wait a bit longer," Kees remarked, "You cannot be careful enough with these newly arrived Nazis." This time they did not return and finally Kees went down below to bring the real patient upstairs to the doctor. After a quick examination he was brought down below again, the doctor had seen the problem in an instant.

"Malnutrition, and nothing we can do about it, other than giving him as many vegetables that you can. Can you get any spinach?"

When Cornelius heard the word spinach he jumped up and shouted, "Yes,

I have, just nice and fresh in my garden here, in my special hothouse!"

Kees had made all the arrangements for the two young ladies and when he and Cornelius went to bring them the news of their transport and their new ID's they were at the apartment above the bookstore. Ina had done a great job on Ilse's hair; the two girls almost looked identical except for the different color of their eyes. "They can pass as twins," Kees agreed. When he had taken their pictures with his old camera, he had to adjust the position of Ilse to have her look more like her newly found 'sister.'

"Tonight at exactly 9 o'clock you will see an ambulance in the back alley of the shop. One of you will have to dress in these clothes," he handed them a bag and explained: "One of you is going to be a nurse, the other needs to be placed on the gurney in the ambulance, tucked in and tightly strapped with most of the face bandaged. These papers here are your transport papers to Cologne in Germany.

"Of course you are not going that far, but the papers have to show a German destination. In Oosterbeek, at your brother's farm, the ambulance will stop to get some food and milk. That will be the excuse to stop there, and you two will get out of the ambulance. That way no one will know that you are there and we need to keep it that way. Of course Ina, you are the legitimate sister of Krelis, not Jewish, so you have nothing to hide. Ilse, on the other hand, has to keep a low profile there at the farm, even though you are the sister of Geert Jansen, a Jew without a star. Krelis does not know that he is Jewish and please, Ina, don't ever tell him the truth about Geert and Ilse. Krelis is against hiding Jews and he might even send the two of you away, if he were to find out. So let's keep the secret until this lousy war is over."

"From now on, Ilse, you will also be a Jew without a star."

Chapter Sixteen

TIGHTENING THE DRAGNET

The long table in the Ridderzaal was covered with papers, official German-issued newspapers. On a separate pile were all the illegal newspapers which the underground press had produced. The Generals had commanded all their secretaries to bring in the latest papers in order to determine if they had been publishing what the headquarters in Berlin had ordered and compare them with what the underground press had been publishing.

One officer picked up the illegal paper called *Trouw* and read aloud:

A prisoner from a concentration camp sent us the following letter:

The camp commander, Chmiliefsky left the camp some time ago. He stole so much money, diamonds, and jewelry from the Jewish prisoners that his loot must amount to many millions. It must have become obvious in Berlin that the yield of Jewish plunder transmitted by Chmiliefsky was suspiciously low. This led to the uncovering of his personal thievery.

The sub commander, Rheinecke was also transferred. Following the example of his chief, he too had enriched himself scandalously. Together with Chmiliefsky and some of the SS officers he held regular drinking bouts and orgies.
The most attractive Jewish girls in the camp were picked out and forced to participate. Erlanger, the substitute Schutzhaftlagerfuhrer (Commander over the police in the camp) who used to amuse himself by entering the barracks and

firing his gun at random, has also disappeared. So he won't be able to enact his personal plans to torture the prisoners in the executioners cages of the newly build prison in the center of the camp.
The Rottenfuehrer, whom we used to call 'Santa,' was known for his cruel beating till death of prisoners, is still here. He does not have that kind of fun anymore because he is becoming aware that the Nazis are never going to win the war.

In the meantime, new scoundrels have been sent from Germany to replace the ones who have left. A certain Adam Gruenewald is now the camp Commander. A couple of weeks ago, this new guy saw fit to rouse all 1200 Jews in the camp in the middle of the night for a roll call. The wretched people were robbed of their last possessions and clothes. Instead they were given dirty and torn underwear without buttons and old convict clothes. The guards even tore off the women's brassieres. Each person received a small piece of bread and then all of them were loaded into a cattle-train wagon. Each wagon had to contain at least sixty people who were pushed inside like sardines in a can. Each wagon had a barrel of water and one cup. The soldiers locked the wagons with extra barbed wire on the outside.

The train was destined for Sobidor in Poland. In all likelihood, those trains are often sidetracked for a week and arrive with their cargo half dead. I am amazed that the Dutch railway workers are willing to cooperate with these inhumane means of transportation.

We sometimes hear news from the outside of the camp, how the free people behave, which makes my stomach turn. I have been told that the number of Dutch girls and women who are flirting with the Germans runs into the tens of thousands and that there are thousands of births of German babies with Dutch mothers. If that is true, I find it disgusting.

When newly arriving prisoners tell us that in all the cinemas they show nothing but Nazi propaganda, it gives me the feeling that even our own people are giving in to the enemy.

Nowadays there are some six thousand prisoners here. Many of them are the so-called Juedenfreunde (friends of the Jews) as the Nazis call them. Most of these people are the scum of the world, common parasites. For example, for five hundred guilders per month they had taken Jews into their homes. When they were found out, they sold the Jews to the Nazis for another five hundred guilders. They dare to tell us that they have become anti-Semites and that all Jews are crooks and extortionists. Those people still dare to call themselves Hollanders.

Joop Franken, Westerbork November 1944

The Nazi who had read the article aloud, laughed a wicked laugh and remarked, "Even the Dutch are turning sour."

Another article was picked up and read aloud:

NSB-er, Mayor of IJsselstein caught in his own tricks.

"That will not happen to me," said the mayor of IJsselstein, two days before the resistance attacked his rationing office. Together with a friend they had personally watched over the safe which contained nine thousand rationing coupons. The attacking Resistance gave him the opportunity to see the safe from the inside while the rationing coupons were taken. He was found very hungry five days later…

Many more illegal papers were read and the mood of the Nazi Generals began to turn very angry. "What are we doing about all these illegal printing presses? They undermine our authority. We must find them and destroy them immediately." A general warning was issued and all Gestapo officers received the following message:

Anyone carrying more than three newspapers needs to be arrested and interrogated until they reveal where the papers came from. No exceptions!

It was the beginning of a new war. This one raged against the press and those who were reading illegal newspapers. The citizens had scarcely been notified of the measure and within a day hundreds of innocent citizens were taken into custody and tortured until they broke. Kees was one of them and for three days he was questioned for having a bundle of newspapers on his bicycle. He kept telling the interrogators that he had found them on the street and that he was only using them to burn in his stove.

He was hit many times and kept awake for three days and two nights when finally his captors gave up. Because of his record as having worked for Symowitz and for never having been arrested before, he was released as a hurt, but not broken individual.

Kees was thankful for the outcome and more determined than ever to fight with all his might against this unjust oppressor. That same night he called a meeting of the Resistance and announced that no children should be exposed to this form of brutality and interrogation so no more newspapers should be delivered by them. "From now on we will only spread newspapers ourselves and at night to prevent further incidents. Now, we need to warn all our illegal presses about the chance of being betrayed," was his final word.

The new draft of Nazis had found a different way of making life unbearable. Instead of making their living quarters in the Dutch Government buildings they seized the houses of the civilians. Kees had an experience he would never forget. In the late fall of 1944 he went to Oegstgeest, a village near the city of Leiden, where several Resistance members were living. His mission was to deliver a large number of food stamps just freshly printed.

As usual, Cornelius was dressed up with many packs of the counterfeit stamps. The little skinny boy came to look like a chunky little guy when Johanna was ready with the preparations. She used four layers of clothing. First he was putting on a shirt so that the paper would not rub on his skin. Then a dress shirt, on the inside of which she had sewed pockets in which the packets of one hundred stamps fitted perfectly. Over the shirt came a sweater and finally a jacket with a zipper which covered everything up. The jacket was water proof, because the food stamps should not get wet.

They mounted the bicycle at 8 a.m. It would normally take an hour and a half to ride the bike to Oegstgeest. This time it took them all day.

The road blocks were everywhere and the soldiers were very meticulous in searching every person who wanted to pass. Several bicycles were being seized. Kees had to talk the soldiers out of the confiscation of his bicycle, every time using his little son as the excuse.

Only one time a soldier had attempted to frisk Cornelius, but he knew what to do. His crying act did the trick each time. When the two finally reached their destination it was getting dark. The late fall in Holland made the evenings come early. By five o'clock the sun had gone down and by six p.m. it was completely dark.

Darkness entailed and curfew had begun, so there would be no way to return to The Hague. There were three addresses where they had to go to deliver their contraband cargo. The houses on the Rijnsburger Weg were beautiful three story villas. That evening was just like any evening during the war. There were no lights coming from the homes; the street lanterns had not been turned on for two years. Darkness was complete. It had its advantages but also its disadvantages. The negatives were that suddenly soldiers could show up without warning. During curfew, any citizen on the street would be arrested at an instant and taken to a local jail for questioning by the feared Gestapo.

The advantage of the total darkness was that the Resistance could use it as a cover. They knew the back alleys where the soldiers did not dare to go. Kees and Cornelius were slowly moving through the alley towards the first villa's back entrance when they heard voices not too far ahead. Quickly Kees pulled Cornelius into a back yard gate, leaving his bicycle against the Liguster hedge.

When the voices came closer he heard German words. They moved further into the backyard, hiding in between the bushes. They also heard a woman's voice and when they saw them pass the gate of the house where they were hiding. Kees saw what was happening. Two soldiers were accompanying two Dutch girls who did not seem to mind being with them. When they passed they were giggling and talking as if they were on a date. Kees walked towards the alley to see where they were going. He was shocked to see them enter through the very gate he had wanted to enter. Why would they be going into a house of one of his Resistance members? Kees intended to find out. He whispered to Cornelius to follow him on foot but not until he had hidden his precious bicycle in the back yard of the villa where they had been hiding.

When they came closer to the villa where his Resistance friend lived they heard the noise of partying coming from the villa. Kees did not dare to ring the doorbell to find out the reason of the unusual situation. He decided to find the next contact address he had food stamps for. It was just ten villas further down the same alley.

They approached the villa on foot and stealthily entered the back yard. It was perfectly still in the house when Kees knocked with the usual code on the back door. It remained still for a long time, Kees knocked again, and then finally he heard a voice behind the door. "We have nothing to give you, go away," a voice was calling in a muted tone. Kees said just one word: "Graag". He thought of the irony of that word in this case. It meant 'please' in Dutch. It was not the customary answer to the words 'go away'. It did the trick though, in a second the door opened wide and a man whom Kees had worked with for all the years of the war pulled Kees and Cornelius quickly inside.

Coen van der Plas used to be a teacher; the war had ended his career at the high school in the town. He had been active as a distributor of food stamps to the hiding places in Oegstgeest and Leiden. Coen had escaped the Arbeits Einsatz by being active as a teacher for the Nazis. It had been an idea of the Resistance to infiltrate the German Occupation and have ears inside the enemy camp. At the same time, Coen had the time to work in the Underground. The Nazis had a desperate need for Dutch interpreters and Coen's teaching did not harm the cause of the Resistance. When he saw Kees and his son at the door he welcomed them enthusiastically. "Kees and son, how great to see you here, sit down and talk to me," he said.

"First of all," Kees began, "Nice to see you in good health. I just found out that at the house of Marten they are operating some kind of bordello; what happened to Marten de Ruiter and his family?"

Coen's face turned sad when he answered the question: "He was kicked out of his house by the Moffen. They are doing that now all over the place. Rather than staying in their barracks, they confiscate the nice houses. The owners are kicked out; they cannot take anything with them. The Moffen with their filthy army boots trample the carpets and everything in the house. They have no regard for someone else's possessions and when they have wrecked the furniture and messed up the house completely they move to the next house. I am lucky because I am known by the Nazis as their teacher, so they have not done it to me."

"So, where did Marten and his family go?" Kees asked.

"They went to live with his mother down town in Leiden. As long as you live in a small house you could be safe, for now, that is. This new bunch of Nazis are bigger crooks than the previous ones. They are determined to destroy as much as they can now that they know they are on a losing streak."

"Are there any other Resistance members who lost their homes here in town?"

"I have not heard of any yet; let's hope this war will soon be over. Have you heard any news about the progress of the Allieds?" Kees told him about the experience he had had by visiting the Canadians in Arnhem and how he had followed them to the Belgian border. Cornelius had fallen asleep on a sofa as the two Resistance fighters caught up in telling each other about all their events from the past few weeks. When Kees ended his story he looked at the clock. Time had flown by; they had both been lost in their recent memories.

Kees looked at his sleeping son and asked if he could stay and sleep in Coen's house. "Of course, I did not expect anything else," Coen answered. "But I have to make one more visit before I can go to bed. If I can leave Cornelius here for just fifteen minutes I will be back quickly."

They never told each other where they were heading in the Resistance, just in case someone would be arrested and interrogated. It is better not to know things then to be forced to tell under pressure of interrogations. "Besides I can do it safer under the cover of darkness then I could tomorrow during daylight."

Kees left quickly. He took the back alleys for more than one kilometer before he had reached the house of his third call. The back door was through a basement so he could safely stand in front of the door and do his knocking ritual. This time he had to knock several times. Finally a sleepy voice called out,"Who is it"? Kees recognized the voice, but he still avoided mentioning his name just in case the voice inside would be coming from a man who had a gun in his back by a Nazi. His code word 'Graag' did the trick as always and within minutes he left the same way he had come. Mission accomplished, except for the first one. He would have to deal with that in the morning.

He did not like to operate in daylight. The word 'underground' had its purpose. The risk of operating in the day time was much greater. The NSB-ers were still active and anywhere where someone entered, the chance of being betrayed was always there.

Kees was back at his host's house in ten minutes. He had run almost all the way, running feather light through the dark. His first question when he arrived was, "Are you familiar with the Dutch girls who entertain the soldiers in Marten's house?"

Coen laughed when he answered, "Not really, for obvious reasons."

They both laughed, "I did not mean in that way. I mean do you know who they are? We need to know for after the war; those traitors need to be rewarded properly." Kees told him about the great number of hungry Dutch citizens in the cities who entertained the Nazis. "In addition to entertaining our enemy they surrender all kinds of information which has repeatedly harmed our organization."

The soldiers in Marten's house were drunk every evening. It seemed they had to drink away their guilt. Many houses which had been confiscated by the Nazi's were turned into brothels or drinking parlors. The Resistance was increasingly angry with this kind of behavior and planned to set an example.

Kees left to go find Marten's mother in Leiden the next morning. Cornelius was excited about seeing Marten's family because there was a boy of his age with whom he used to have a great time when they were still living in their house. He did not understand why the Germans were living in the home of Mr. Marten, as he used to call him. After he had undressed himself to unload the rest of the counterfeit food stamps, Cornelius went to play with his little friend.

"What are you planning to do about the seizure of your house?" Kees asked him when they were alone in the upstairs room which Marten and his family now called their home.

"That is something I want to discuss with you because my colleagues here in the Resistance are planning an attack on my home late at night when the

Nazis are all drunk. I am afraid it will further destroy my house and may lead to severe repercussions. I realize we have to set an example to dissuade the Nazis of taking more homes for their vile behavior. I just hate to ruin my house in the process. What do you think, Kees?"

"Are the soldiers acting with the consent of their superiors or are they doing these seizures on their own accord?" Kees was thinking aloud. "We should find out if the leaders approve of it or even know about it or not. If they have given the orders we should be very careful in attacking them. If they act on their own they might even be condemned by their own generals. In the latter case the generals might even punish the soldiers. I won't hold my breath about that, but it would and might prevent repercussions. What are the other Resistance people saying about that and has anyone inquired who, if anyone, gave the orders to take our homes?"

"You are opening a can of worms so to speak, but I agree that we will have to do a lot more homework before we plan a definite attack." Marten replied, "Do you know of anyone who had access to the generals in The Hague? Is there perhaps a policeman who works for us who could find out about the house seizures?"

Kees promised to look into the matter and warned Marten, "Don't do anything until I get back to you, promise? I really believe that if you take any action we need to know what follows after it. We don't want to have the blood of our own citizens on our hands. Do you understand?"

"Those were wise words you spoke, Kees. I very much appreciate your input in the matter. I am anxious to get my house back but I would not want anybody to be harmed in the process. I will warn the others not to take any action until you report back to me; I hope it will be soon. Thank you, Kees." With those words Kees and Cornelius departed. The return to The Hague was becoming more difficult every day. The Germans never found any reason to arrest Kees, and Cornelius enjoyed riding with his dad. The Nazis never bothered the little boy on the back seat of the bicycle. In fact more often they seemed jealous of the father and son relationship they were unable to have for themselves.

Chapter Seventeen

HUNGER IS TAKING ITS TOLL

—෴—

The Nazis were hungry themselves. Their Heimat, (Homeland) could not supply any food. The distribution system failed. The food production in Holland had come to a dead stop.

The new Nazis which had arrived in The Hague were meaner than ever. They were those that had been brought up in Germany as the so called "Hitler Juegent". These youngsters had great pride in, and expectations of, the Third Reich. They were all the perfect Aryans as Hitler had envisioned. Their hatred against the Dutch and the Dutch Jews had been indoctrinated into them in the youth camps of the Nazis.

These Nazi soldiers were not married and their ties to their families were only based on their education by the Nazi freaks, who had taught them that 'The Reich' was first and foremost above any family ties. They were brought up to betray their parents if they had to. They were indoctrinated that they should kill their brother or sister if they would not conform to the rules of The Reich.

When they had finally been released as Nazi soldiers and sent to Holland, their cruelty knew no boundaries. Little did they know about the stubborn Dutch, about the mentality of the Dutch farmers and the determination of the Dutch working class. When hunger became the primary problem for the Dutch, the New Nazis poured fuel on the fire by confiscating all food supplies.

They had to learn their lessons the hard way when they began to visit the farms south of The Hague with a band of soldiers and trucks. They confiscated all the cows which had been left by the previous soldiers who had wanted to give the farmers at least a small chance to continue their trade. The news about the confiscations of all the livestock at the farms was brought to the attention of Kees, who in turn made it known to the Resistance.

One evening in October of 1944, a meeting was held at the farm of one of the victimized farmers in Delft. It was a secret meeting and the farmers came from all over the Province of South Holland. They came mostly on foot, through the meadows and orchards. Kees had not seen that many people together in one place since before the war. Luckily the farm was far away from the town and out of the reach of normal traffic.

The local farmers had come in an angry mood; some were screaming at the men of the Resistance, demanding action. Kees knew from past experiences that an angry crowd did not help in the cause of the Resistance. Many times before, a riot had resulted in dead bodies and many arrests. The four men of the Resistance withdrew to a nearby pigsty, which had also been robbed empty but still smelled of the pungent hog dung.

Kees's first words were, "Does anyone have any suggestions how we can help these angry farmers, or rather, how we could protect them from creating a riot?"

Frans, the handyman of the Resistance who always had a reasonable solution for any situation exclaimed, "This mob of farmers will be hard to control, unless we can convince them that they are asking for more trouble than they will be able to handle."

Karel de Third was a young, but very smart person. Before the war he had studied Human Relationships at the University of Leiden. He had a knack to predict what people were thinking and he had a very wise approach to often difficult situations. "What we should do firstly, is to listen to what they have to say and how they plan on doing something about it. After all, these people have lost their means of existence. They have a right to be angry so let them talk for a while, and in the mean time we will think of something."

The four men all agreed to the last suggestion. When they returned to the stable where the noisy meeting was going on, nothing had changed. The farmers were still demanding action. Kees waved both his hands to the crowd and with a loud voice he yelled, "Gentlemen, let's sit down on the floor and bring some order to this meeting." The crowd finally listened and settled down. After at least five more minutes there was only one voice which could be heard. It was the voice of Kees who held the attention of the farmers as he spoke, "My dear fellow countrymen, we sympathize with your predicament. For those who have been the victim of these Nazi looters I can only say that you have the right to avenge yourselves."

Several people in the stable shouted in agreement. Kees continued, "If you want to do something you will have to outsmart the enemy, because a direct fight with them will not succeed. On the contrary, we will lose much more than we already have."

Kees could tell by the responses that were made that he had their attention. "I have an idea, but we must first get some answers from you. First of all how are the Nazis going about it? Are they systematically going from farm to farm, or are they randomly hitting your places?" Several remarks came at the same time and as Kees saw the ones who gave the answers, he asked them to come forward and make their statement one by one.

After having heard the accounts of what had occurred from eight farmers and while using a map of the area to point out where the Nazis had hit, it was clearly showing that the Nazis were going from West to East, hitting every farm systematically. Frans, who had drawn the map and followed the progress of the enemy, made the remark when he had seen the order in which the Nazis were going to work. "They are just going to every farm, leaving no one untouched," he proclaimed, "We can do something with that!"

After a lot of murmurs, loud protests and discussions back and forth among the farmers in the stable, they quieted down once more. Meanwhile, the four Resistance men had conferred together. Kees took the floor again and began, "Gentlemen I think we may have a temporary solution but we will have to work diligently tonight to bring it into practice."

"Here is what we propose: At one night you must bring your livestock to one of the farms which has already been hit. You will have to sacrifice a few of your animals, because if the Nazis find nothing anywhere, they may begin to wonder where your livestock is. As a result they may take you to their Gestapo headquarters and give you a thorough interrogation. If you know what that means you would not want that to happen. So far no one has ever come out alive from one of those sessions. We need four men who are willing to coordinate this plan and as the Nazis move further, we will have to find other groups of four in the region."

The farmers began to talk to each other again and for a long time the noise of dozens of farmers arguing and discussing options filled the room. For the four Resistance fighters it was a long and painful wait for the outcome. Dutch farmers were known to be stubborn and each of them would have his own opinion on how to solve the present situation.

When, once again the crowd in the stable had become quiet, one of the farmers remained standing and began to address the men who were leading the discussions. "We, at least those in the group I was sitting with, are not interested in your suggestion. We think it will be a sign of weakness to the Nazis if we don't act more aggressively." The crowd became dead silent when the speaker announced, "Most of us have guns and other weapons and we feel we should attack the slaughterhouse where our livestock has gone. We want to teach the Nazis a lesson they will never forget. We realize that we cannot take our cows back, we don't have trucks like they do, but we could shoot every animal in the slaughterhouse along with every worker and Nazi we encounter. Then, and then alone, will they respect us as farmers and return to buying our animals instead of stealing them."

The speech had made a great impact on the people and it resulted once more in a lot of shouting and yelling. Arguments began to take over the normal conversation.

The four men of the Resistance looked at each other and shook their heads. "This is going nowhere, and if anything, it is going in a completely opposite direction from what we had been planning." They had all stood up and groups began to form among the farmers. Apparently there were those who were choosing the nonaggressive option. But after what seemed like hours there finally was a large group who had decided on their way to solve the situation. When at last one of them spoke, Kees could not believe his ears at what was proposed.

"We all agree now that the only way we want to take action is by planning an attack on the slaughterhouse in The Hague, and we want the Resistance to help us in the plan and its execution. You people have the experience and the know-how to set this thing up, and we are counting on you."

Kees had quickly conversed with his colleagues and was preparing to answer the farmers on their proposal. Kees felt the great pressure he was under; an attack was not his kind of work. He did not know how to tell these angry farmers that an attack was not the solution. He had never approved of that kind of resistance and he was certainly not going to participate in it this time. He told the other three that he was willing to address the crowd with an answer, but that he needed some time alone to pray about it. He told Frans that he would go outside for ten minutes and asked him to tell the audience to take a break until he came back.

Kees stepped into the dark orchard and walked in between the trees. The dark night sky was full of stars. He thought of Abraham, how God had told him to look up into the sky at the stars and remembered the promise He had given him, *your seed will become as many as the stars you can see in the sky...*

What did that have to do with his talk to the farmers? He wondered and he prayed, "Lord, please grant me the wisdom you gave to Abraham and explain to me what you mean with that Bible text."

When he walked back into the stable he knew the answer and the warning he would have to give the men who were so anxious to put their lives on the line. His three colleagues knew Kees very well, they were familiar with his faith walk, and they trusted him with his judgment of the situation. They knew what he was going to say. It had become very still in the large stable where more than fifty farmers were in anticipation of a plan of attack.

When Kees began to speak you could hear a pin drop in the previously noisy stable, where so many farmers had vented their anger.

"Gentlemen, you may or may not know that I am a devout Christian and what I am going to tell you may not be what you would like to hear. When I went out into the orchard just minutes ago the Lord gave me a vision. It was a Bible-based vision that I am sure most of you have heard before.

"When Abraham was visited one day by God, He took him outside and asked him to look at the stars in the sky. You can imagine how that looked at a time when there were no distracting lights on the ground, no search lights in the sky looking to shoot planes down, just a still clear night sky with millions of stars. God gave Abraham a vision and a promise that, even though he did not have any children at that time, he would be blessed with children and he would be multiplied to a great nation with as many people as the stars in the sky.

"I too had that vision when I walked outside and I wondered what it meant in this time and age of violence, instead of a time of peace. I realized that God showed me that, should you make an attack as you are contemplating, you would not see your children multiplied like the stars in the sky." It had become very still in the stable.

"My colleagues and I are non-violent Resistance men. We have never killed a Nazi and we will never approve of any attack. Not only because we would have to kill Nazis, but we would also have to kill innocent slaughterhouse civilians and the consequences that will follow will be even greater. Any attack made by the Resistance has previously caused repercussions on the population. You know that the Nazis will take civilians from the neighborhood of the slaughterhouse and execute at least as many as the soldiers that would be killed in the attack. Gentlemen, my dear fellow citizens, I strongly advise against any form of attack."

When Kees stopped talking it was quiet for a minute. Then several men began to yell and scream in protest of what Kees had said. Some of them were raising their fists against the men of the Resistance. After several minutes one of the farmers came forward and raised his hands trying to calm down the group of angry men. It took him at least five minutes until he could speak, even then he had to raise his voice to be heard, "Friends, don't listen to these guys," he began, "We cannot allow the Nazis to ruin our businesses. We are here now with only fifty victims of their looting; tomorrow they will add another ten and everyday thereafter, at least ten more of our fellow farmers will be put out of business. Some might be killed in the process and we all will die of hunger when the Nazis keep stealing our livestock. Besides, what will be next? They might come to pick us all up for their labor camps. Then our wives will die of hunger and so will our children. There won't be enough stars in the sky to amount to our dead bodies.

"We have to do something and we will have to do it now or all hell will break loose and cause more havoc than we can handle." Many voices were raised again, everyone had a different opinion. Then another farmer took the floor and began to speak, "I agree with the previous speaker. We must take action now, but I feel we need advice from the militant part of the Resistance. I respect Kees and his friends here, but what we need is help from the guys of the Boxers, and I know one of the leaders. We could take Kees' advice for just one or two nights, we would distract the Nazis for a few days and that will give us time to get a plan together with the Boxers. I am sure I can get them to come here tomorrow night."

This time a lot of approving comments could be heard. Kees saw a change in attitude in the crowd and he said to Frans, "We need to leave now. Our assistance is no longer needed here, and hopefully they will do what we advised and find out that it will work for the time being. I won't hold my breath about what the Boxers will come up with." He walked over to the front of the audience and waved his hands to request them to be quiet.

When Kees spoke he felt at least that they were willing to listen. "I think you have reached a good compromise and if you take your time and make no rash decisions, the Lord will bless you with wisdom and guidance. We have to go now; if you want we can also get you in touch with the Boxers. We thank you for listening and may God bless you." With those words the four Resistance men left the stable and after a brief talk outside, each of them went their separate way. In those dark times and after curfew it was best not to walk in groups or even in two's.

It was after midnight when Kees came home. Johanna was waiting in the front room and wanted to hear what had happened that evening. Kees told her about the anger he had seen in the gathering of farmers and how he had had a vision from God about the stars in heaven. "I hope they will think about that part of my talk because if they go to make an attack it will be a blood bath. Let's go to sleep, because tomorrow morning I need to visit the Boxers leader here in The Hague to tell him what the farmers want to do and prepare him for a confrontation. I know they would want to take action, but they need to know that the consequences will be huge and that many will lose their lives."

Cornelius was up early the next day. His back yard farm needed some attention, he had decided. His kale plants were getting really big and the day before he had seen the damage some caterpillars had done to them. He could not allow that to happen. He was meticulously searching each plant for the caterpillars and stomped them under his feet when he found them. He reflected about what he was doing. Isn't that the just the same thing as what the German soldiers were doing in his country? They too were eating away at the food that was not theirs, while his father and the other Resistance people were searching the Nazis out and crushing them under their feet?

Or were they not?

Kees came walking into Cornelius' little farm and asked him what he was doing. "Daddy, I am just like the Resistance now. I am crushing the enemy which is taking the food that does not belong to them, just like you are doing."

His father looked at his little boy and wondered, where does he get this wisdom from? He is such a wise little boy; what will become of this little guy if this war goes on much longer? That day Kees kept thinking about what his son had said… What was the message he had given him? Was he doing the right thing by advising the farmers not to attack, *not to try to crush the enemy?* Kees was thinking of that when he visited the leader of the Boxers that morning. He began to think in favor of an attack, even though he was a non-violent person. Was this war changing his morality? Could he become militant as well?

He decided to deal with that thought that evening by reading the Bible and praying about it together with Johanna. He might even include his smart little son in the discussion.

The leader of the Boxers had seen Kees coming through an opening in his curtains. He knew Kees well and had several discussions with him in the past. He knew Kees was anti violence and that he had always avoided it. He wondered what he had experienced this time and if Kees would ever change his mind on how they could win this war.

The two Resistance friends greeted each other solemnly. Leo van der Wal was a stout man who had long arms and when he embraced someone his arms could go around the other person twice. Kees felt as though he was a short and skinny man under Leo's embrace. The two were fond of each other and they had great respect for each other's activities in the underground.

Leo asked Kees to take a seat and offered him some surrogate coffee. "I already know about your visit with the farmers," he began "and I sort of figured you would show up this morning. They beat you by one hour. What do you think of the situation, Kees?"

The remark came unexpectedly and Kees was not prepared to answer. "Why have they come so quickly, Leo? What is their plan now? Do they still want to go ahead with an attack?"

"I am afraid so" Leo answered, "and they want our help. They also told me that you did not approve of an attack, but I must say there is no chance of keeping these stubborn guys from taking action. For goodness sake, Kees, they lost their means of income, their business. How can a farmer be a farmer without livestock? And even more so, they see the Nazis coming for days on end taking all the other farmers' animals as well. They can't even buy from each other in that case. The Nazis are eliminating their entire trade, systematically and methodically. After that, the Nazis have reasons to arrest them and send them to the work camps, too."

Kees answered him in a timid way: "I know what you are saying, but you know that I would do anything to avoid confrontations and fights with the Nazis. You know the consequences, the repercussions and the number of dead on both sides could be huge. I came here to get your advice on how to handle this thing peacefully. Has anyone tried to talk to the Nazis? Who could we send to negotiate this?"

"As it stands at the present time, any one we would send would simply be arrested; you know how these new young Nazi punks are." You better leave this matter to us. We, the Boxers, will set it up in such a way that the Nazis will never know what hit them. We are finalizing the plan, and tonight it is going to happen. No more slaughter house means they cannot handle the cows, can they?"

"But what about the aftermath?" Kees uttered barely audibly.

"We will deal with that, too. Believe me, Kees. We do have a great plan; relax and get out of the way. You'll see soon."

Kees let out a huge sigh and turned around to leave his friend when the head Boxer added, "Hey Kees, no personal hard feelings, I hope. You do your job in your way and we do ours in our way. We have always respected each other's ways. Let's not change that attitude, okay?"

On the way back to his house Kees was thinking hard. Who could be sent to the German general or to Seiss Inquart, the Nazi appointed governor, to negotiate? Was there anyone neutral enough to send? He racked his mind for hours that day, but he could not think of anyone to send. Could he do it himself? The answer came to his mind immediately, emphatically no! Then he asked himself, why not? The answer to the last question came when he arrived at home to find both his wife and his son crying.

He was very hungry when he walked into his small city home in the Deiman Straat. He heard them crying before he saw them and wondered what had happened. His inquisitive look posed the question before he even asked. "We cannot get anymore food," said Johanna and put her head on his shoulders. "This morning I went to the butcher, he had nothing to sell, and then I went to the baker; he had nothing at all for sale. I went to seven stores and no one had any food for sale. We have an obligation to the eight people down stairs, Kees. What are we going to do?" She cried aloud now and Cornelius did also. Taking his father's hand he cried as he spoke, "Let's go to the farm, Dad, and get some food. I am so hungry. Please."

After this sad confrontation, Kees realized that he had not eaten for more than two days either. Now he realized how hungry he was. He made the decision to go to the Hoekse Waard, a farm area south of Rotterdam and further away from the region the Nazis had been looting. He would take his son with him and leave right away. He felt good about it also, because he would no longer have to deal with the pending farmers' attack.

Half an hour later at nine a.m. they left the city. Kees felt he had already had a day's work behind him. The thought of riding through the fields toward the farms which had not been hit yet would give him enough energy to face the next day and the news he expected to hear about.

Cornelius was happy to be on the back of the bicycle again even though he was very hungry; the fresh air of the beautiful countryside and the cozy seat behind his father's broad back gave him a feeling of complete happiness.

The first barricade they came to was easy; of course they had nothing to hide this time. The Nazis looked puzzled at Kees's wallet which contained a few hundred guilders. The soldier seemed to hesitate to let him go with all that money. When Kees saw the man's hesitation he said: "I have to bring that to my father who lives in Oud Beierland. He is old and has to pay the doctor, but he has no income." The soldier looked at the two on the bicycle and thought, *I hope my father still lives through all the bombardments back in Germany. I wish I was able to bring him some money and go see him.* He told Kees to go and even gave a friendly greeting, "Gueten tag, du beide," and waved them on with his hand.

That day they had eight road blocks to deal with before they came to the town of Oud Beierland. It was the birth place of Kees. He knew almost all the people in the area. Wherever he went he was greeted with surprise and friendliness. When he came to the shop his brother Dirk was operating in the town, he saw a long line outside the shop. Here in this town he had never expected lines in front of the stores. Kees went around the store through an alley to the back entrance.

What he saw there startled him. Two German soldiers were smoking cigarettes and seemed to watch anyone coming and going. They had a notebook in which they wrote the name of the person coming out of the shop and registered each article they had purchased.

When Kees attempted to enter the back door he was stopped by the two soldiers. They asked for his Ausweiss and pointed him to the front of the store. Kees shook his head and said: "I came to visit my brother and I want to go upstairs to his apartment."

One of the soldiers went inside and came back with Dirk, the brother of Kees. When they saw each other is was obvious they were family. Dirk looked greatly surprised he gave Kees a big hug, and then Cornelius. Then he said, "What a great surprise to see you two here all the way from The Hague. You must go upstairs, Dina is there and she will give you something to eat." It sounded like music to Cornelius' ears. Food, he had that word on his mind for the last three days without getting his hands on any. The soldier was convinced they were family and let them go through. Dirk said, "Sorry, Kees, I will have to tend the store; I am all by myself and there is a long line up in front. I should be done in an hour or so. It won't take long, the store will be empty soon." He shrugged his shoulders, "There won't be anything left to sell."

Dirk went back to the difficult task of distributing the food he had in his store. He returned to too many customers with too many problems and too much inspection from the Nazis. His clients were patient, but as they saw the store emptying out they became restless and started to shout: "Leave me a loaf of bread, Dirk," or, "I really need some butter Dirk; keep some for me before you sell it all." Dirk had no choice. The soldier next to him checked every food stamp and allocation Dirk made. The people at the end the line outside had to be told to go home or find another store to purchase what they needed. Some people had stood in line at three different stores that day. They still had to go home empty handed.

When the entire inventory was gone, the soldiers had to push the remaining people out of the store so Dirk could lock it up. The soldiers left and for one week there would be nothing for sale until the allocation truck, a Nazi vehicle, would come and sparsely stock up the store. The same scene would occur. People would line up on the street, sometimes four hours before Dirk could open the store. He was not allowed to open his doors until the soldiers arrived.

Kees and Cornelius had filled their bellies upstairs and were visiting with Dirk's wife, Dina. She was explaining how the system of distribution was controlled by the Nazis and that it was very difficult to keep back any food for themselves and their family.

"You see, the Nazis have registered every pound of food, whether it is butter, bread, cheese, meat or vegetables. All the distribution stamps allow one pound of something. When the load of food comes in, it arrives at night so that the customers can not interfere with the unloading. The truck is coming with armed guards and in some cases, luckily not at our store, fights have occurred where people tried to steal the food from the truck while they were unloading."

When she was about to explain how they were able to get some food for themselves and for their family, even some for a hiding place with Jews, Dirk came upstairs with tears in his eyes, "I don't know how long I can keep up with this charade. All my friends here in town are beginning to hate me. I do everything I can for them, but those Nazis get on my nerves all the time; Thank God I have a week in between to distribute the food. I hate it, but now I have been told that there will be no more meat coming. That is what the two soldiers told me, and when I asked them why, they told me that the livestock availability was coming to an end. What does that mean, Kees?"

"That is one of the reasons I came here today," Kees answered him. "From The Hague a new garrison of soldiers has been employed to take all the animals from the farmers. Last night I had a meeting with fifty farmers from around the city of Delft. They had been visited by the Nazis who came with big army trucks and loaded up all their livestock. Previously they would only take a few and leave the farmers with something to work with. Now they are putting them completely out of business and the next thing is that the farmers don't need to be at their farms anymore, so the Nazis can take them to their labor camps as well."

"Do you think that that is the reason why we are not getting any meat anymore even though there are still a lot of cows, sheep and pigs everywhere in this country?" Dirk asked.

"What is happening is very serious. The Nazis are shipping all the meat to Germany, to feed their population as well as the army. The main slaughterhouse in The Hague is the center stage for these activities and the Nazis have prepared special cooling trains which transport the meat to Germany."

"Wow!" was all Dirk exclaimed. "Wow, and woe to the Nazis, because if they get all the farmers against them, they will have a big fight on their hands. So the soldiers who were here today already know what is going to happen to our farmers? Isn't there anyone who can talk to the Nazis and bring them to their senses?"

When Kees answered him his voice sounded very grave, "We have thought of that, too, and we realize that with the mentality of the Nazis, and in particular the ones who are in charge now, they would arrest anyone we sent to negotiate. These guys, including their leadership, are fanatics. They do exactly what the High Command in Berlin tells them to, no matter what.

"I still would like to know how you get to keep food for yourself, and for me," Kees said with a smile, as he directed his question to Dina. Before she spoke she looked at her husband with an unspoken question in her eyes. Dirk merely nodded and she began to explain:

"Everything, as I was saying when Dirk walked in, is packed in lots of half a kilo. We take a little bit out of every bag and put it aside for ourselves and our family and friends. I know it sounds unfair and like stealing, but all we do is distribute food in a reasonable way in order to keep people alive. I hope God will forgive us if this is considered sin."

"So what is going to happen with the farmers tonight, Kees?"

"I really don't know the facts. All I know is that I did not want to stay in the city when all hell breaks loose tonight. The farmers have talked with the Boxers, and so have I, and together they are planning an attack on the slaughterhouse. I don't approve of things like that, but I could not persuade them not to do it. As you know, the Nazis always take innocent people from the surrounding areas of an attack and execute them. I would not want to be the cause of the death of innocent civilians and I really don't know if it is going to have the desired effect they are aiming for. To stop the Nazis from an implemented program, sounds to me, like an impossibility."

Kees had stopped talking and looked around in anticipation of what his brother was going to offer him in the way of food to take to the city. Dirk noticed his searching look and inquired, "How many Jews do you have to feed right now? And how many mouths do you have at home in your family?"

"In fact, there are only the three of us, because three of my children have gone to the province of Friesland. I hope the Nazis have not started their meat gathering there yet. In all, I need food for ten people for one week; can you provide that if I come back here every week?"

Dirk was laughing aloud now, "I don't know for the coming weeks. Life goes by the day now, even here. I can give you enough for the coming week, but how are you going to take it? The Nazis will take it from you, you know that."

Kees had a smile on his face this time, "I have my carrier," and pointed at Cornelius. "We can dress him up with most of the food on his body, and he sits on a seat on my bicycle which has a special hidden box under it. Furthermore, I have double side bags on my bicycle and we can fill those with the kinds of things the Nazis don't like."

"It sounds like you have it all worked out, when do you want us to start packing?" Dirk asked.

"Well, eh… can we stay here for the night? I would kind of … like to… look around in the village tomorrow and leave when it gets dark tomorrow night." Kees announced.

"It sounds like you really have a plan. Yes, you two can stay here and yes, we can pack tomorrow just before dark. Now let's enjoy our stay together. Dina can you make us some coffee?"

"Coffee?" Kees repeated.

"Yes, the real thing. I managed to hoard a bit of that two years ago and we still have some time to go on it."

This time Kees said only one word, "Wow."

Chapter Eighteen

THE BLOODBATH AT THE SLAUGHTER HOUSE

At the farm which was far into the fields, behind the apple orchards and invisible from the road, there were more people than a few days before. The farmers had notified many others to come about a matter of most urgency. The message had also said to come between the hours of eight and nine in the evening and to not approach the farm from the road.

They came and had been coming for an hour, through the fields and through the orchards. They jumped the creeks and whenever they heard vehicles on the nearby road they hid themselves behind shacks and trees or hay stacks. It was a risky think to gather with that many people and everyone had taken the utmost care not to be seen by anyone.

It was not only the Nazis they had to hide from. It was also from the collaborators, the feared NSB-ers, who were to be avoided at any cost. Some had come as far as twenty kilometers from their own farms. The message had been clear: *For your own sake and for the future of your farm, be there.*

The meeting was led by Leo van der Wal, the leader of the Boxers from The Hague who had come with six other members of his group. They were the hardened fighters who had more than once led attacks against the German occupation. Usually they had broken into public offices which had been taken over by the Nazis and which contained information and documents which had been needed by the Resistance.

When Leo opened the meeting the farmers had to be quieted down. With so many people of one trade together, they had a lot to talk about. At this time during the war the threat of the Nazi looting had become so great that each of the farmers feared the near future and each of them had a different idea to escape the threat.

Leo welcomed all those present with the patriotic: *Lang leve the Koningin* (Long live the Queen). All those present repeated the words enthusiastically. Leo went directly into the reason for the meeting. "We are all here because the Nazis have begun the new and unacceptable practice of stealing all the livestock from your farms. Apparently two days ago you held a meeting at this very same farm after fifty of you had lost all your livestock. You had invited the Resistance to help you with this problem. Unfortunately, you had invited the wrong branch of the Resistance and the meeting had been adjourned without a resolution as to what should be done about the crisis.

"This time you have reached the right people," he slapped himself on his chest with a smile and went on. "We understand that you want to end this Nazi offensive against your animals and that you are willing to accept our assistance with the plan. Well, we can help you as follows: Tomorrow evening we will attack the slaughterhouse in The Hague and we need you all to be there. If you have a weapon I would like to hear from you at this point. My assistants will come around and take your information. We need to know your name and what kind of weapon you have. In order to coordinate this plan we need that information to put each one into the right position. If you don't have a weapon, let us know, and we will provide you with one. Let us get this done right now. Gentlemen." He gestured at his co-workers to begin their job immediately.

It took all of an hour to gather the information and when the noise swelled to an unacceptable level Leo had to shout and ask them to be quiet. Even that far from the road, the risk of being heard was present and the last thing they needed was a visit from a Nazi platoon.

In the mean time, Leo had hung a map of the area on the wall where the slaughterhouse was located. He had made a large drawing on the back of a roll of wallpaper. He had drawn x's where the entrances and exits were and arrows where the roads led to the facility. The day before they had scouted out the facility and they had made a provisionary count of the number of military who were guarding the place. They had found that three trucks with soldiers were stationed there. Each truck brought somewhere between twenty and thirty soldiers to the facility.

Even though the slaughterhouse was guarded by the military, the everyday operation was managed by civilians, led by the collaborators, commonly called the NSB-ers. There were also the factory workers who had to pledge loyalty to the Nazis in order to get a job. Perhaps a few of the workers were loyal Dutchmen who were faking loyalty to the Nazis. One of those was known by the Resistance and he had received a visit from one of Leo's men. The man had been very cooperative and after he had given as much information as he could about the plant, Leo had asked him to come with him to his "office".

The Boxers had their "office and training facility" in an abandoned school which had been bombed. The three story building had partially collapsed; where once the classrooms had been was now a mountain of rubble. The Nazis had the forced laborers place a fence around the school to avoid the population from taking wood out of the rubble for their fireplaces. In the back of the building was a door which led into the basement. This door was still intact and had been boarded up with planks.

When Leo had found the place they had carefully kept the boarding planks in place, but the door could be opened even though it looked as though it was boarded up. Once they entered the hallway through that door it was only fifty meters to the gym which had not sustained any damage from the falling rubble. It had become the center of training, planning and the arsenal of the Boxers of The Hague.

It was to this "office" where the two had gone, the worker from the slaughterhouse and Leo. The Boxers never took a risk, and leaving an informed person in his place would mean taking a risk. The man did not know it, but once he entered the "office" of the Boxers, he would be kept there until the attack had been performed. Neither did he know that after he would be set free, he would no longer have a job with his former employer.

At the former gym some of the showers had been reinforced to become jail cells. A permanent staff was present who would take care of the prisoners. Some of the prisoners were kept there for their own protection. After each attack by the Boxers those who had assisted them were rewarded for their help, even while they were in captivity. If they so desired they could become honorary members of the Boxers. However if they turned out to be traitors, or they had just been uncooperative, they were dealt with appropriately.

The men of the Boxers who had taken the information from the farmers about their weapons had finished their task. Leo once again quieted the audience and began to speak, "Gentlemen, now that we have your information we will prepare our plan. For that we will need all night and all day tomorrow. We ask you to be back here at the same time tomorrow night. Bring your weapons, dress in black and wear hats. Bivac hats are preferred, but if you don't have one, we will bring some tomorrow night.

"Speak with no one tomorrow and tell your wives goodbye because some of you may not return home." The last remark caused a barrage of questions to be asked and Leo answered them patiently. One of them asked what was exactly going to happen. Leo answered him: "If you want to stay behind and talk to me in private I will tell you. Lastly, gentlemen, please leave now and go carefully two at the time. Make sure that if you are stopped by the Nazis, to tell them that you went to your mother–in–law's birthday; nothing else, please."

The situation was too serious to laugh; just a few of them suppressed a smile. When they had all gone, the man who had the specific questions came to Leo and asked him again, "Please tell me the details of what we are going to do now, so I can think about it over night and perhaps improve upon it."

Before the man had ended his question, two of the other Boxer members had grabbed him and tied him up. "Sorry," Leo said, "we do not give specifics until just before the event. Since you asked, we will have to assume that you want to know so you can tell others, perhaps NB-ers? We cannot risk that and for that reason we are offering you a voluntary stay in our 'office' for a couple of days." The man protested and tried to fight the arrest, but he was no match for the two Boxers.

That evening a German ambulance arrived at the farm an hour after the Boxers had left. One patient was loaded into the ambulance. When it left it did not use its sirens and when it arrived at the bombed school in The Hague, the patient was quickly carried through the boarded door. A second shower door was opened and locked behind the 'voluntary' prisoner. The Boxers had learned their lessons in previous preparations; they knew when someone became too inquisitive.

After the crowd of farmers had gone, the team of Boxers sat down and began to discuss how the attack was going to take place. "The first plan we have to discuss is how we are going to get all these farmers to the slaughterhouse. We should make use of the two German army trucks we have at the airport," one of them proposed.

"That would make sense, but how are we going to load up all these farmers without some NSB-er seeing it?" Leo brought up. "What if we make it look as if we are loading up cattle at one of the farms?"

After several hours of discussion the plan was complete. They had determined to bring the trucks to a farm where they still had a lot of cows and have all the men meet there for the transport to the slaughterhouse.

The chosen farm was visited and the viability to load up the farmers had become clear. The time was set in such a way that all the participating farmers would be able to go to the dedicated farm on foot from the place where they had their first meeting.

They decided to continue their further planning at the Boxers' "office" in the city. They worked all night; every angle of the attack was studied and either refused or accepted. When they finally had all the plans in place and a chronology had been put together, it was four o'clock in the morning. "We better get some sleep because tomorrow we will still have some ground to cover. Our withdrawal from the scene has to be smooth and quick. When we use the army trucks again and if someone would see us coming we could be in serious trouble. It might be better to sacrifice the trucks and have everyone go their separate ways.

"Let's get some shut-eye now and reconvene in the morning. I think we can do it successfully, but we need to inform the farmers how we expect them to get out of there."

The two prisoners at the "office" of the Boxers were both very unhappy about their fate. Even though the two had eaten better than they would have at their homes; each of them was angry about their incarceration. The two had been talking to each other through the thin wall of the former shower stall. The man who worked at the slaughterhouse had asked: "Why are you being held here?"

The farmer from the south had told him that the Boxers wanted him to stay there so that he would not be interrogated by the Gestapo. After several cordial questions the man from the slaughterhouse began to feel uneasy. It seemed as though the farmer's question became too specific; it sounded like he was against the attack.

Neither of the men knew that in the showerheads above their heads, microphones were registering every word that was exchanged and the entire conversation was recorded on a tape recorder just ten feet away. The person in charge of the recorder was hearing every word which was said. He too was becoming increasingly more aware that the farmer was asking too many questions. He intended to report his finding to Leo the next morning.

On the day marked A-Day by the Boxers, five trucks left the encampment of the Nazis located south of the airport Ypenburg. They were large army trucks, three of which were loaded with a total of sixty armed soldiers. In each truck a machine gun was bolted down. The rear flap was tied shut so no one could see the men or the machine guns. The two other trucks were empty. Behind the canvas flap on the back of the trucks were steel gates which turned into a ramp on which animals could walk up into the truck.

The two trucks headed for the southwest area of Holland.

At the repair shop in the hangar at the airport two similar trucks were being prepared for departure. No steel gates or machine guns were in these trucks.

They were of the same make and model as the five trucks which had left the garrison just minutes before.

The farmers saw the trucks coming up on the driveway. They knew what was coming and they feared what was about to happen. The soldiers poured out of the three trucks and commanded the farmer and his wife and children to stay inside the farm house. The commander barked a command and half of the soldiers were dispersed into all the stables of the farm. One cow came out of the stable being hit and pushed to move by the soldiers towards the waiting truck; coming out of another building, soldiers had found some rabbits. Another group of soldiers had found a goat. It seemed it was all they could find. The commander screamed for the farmer to come out of the house and demanded an answer why there were so few animals at his farms. The farmer just shrugged his shoulders and said in broken German "Allen todd, nieghts mehr."(All dead, nothing left).

The feared convoy of Nazi trucks left on their way to the next farm, the next victims of their looting spree. The commander experienced at least nine more farms that day which had hardly any livestock, until he came to one which had a large number of animals. By that time, it had become nearly the end of the day. Finally, the trucks had been filled to capacity and they were able to take their stolen heist to their final destination at the slaughterhouse in The Hague.

Only two trucks went to the slaughterhouse; the trucks with the soldiers went back to the Garrison. By the time they reached the slaughterhouse it had become pitch dark on this moonless evening. That night the street lights did not come on. An all city blackout had been ordered, because of a rumor that an air attack was to be expected.

Under the cover of darkness, two more trucks went on their way towards the farms in the south of Holland. There were only two soldiers in each truck, a driver and a co-driver which was the usual way for Nazi trucks on the road. They knew exactly where they were going.

At the farm where the meetings had been held, men in black clothing were gradually arriving. Some of them were carrying gunnysacks. They entered the same stable and were greeted by Leo and his Boxers. They kept coming in two at a time and appeared as if coming out of nowhere. When the first fifty were inside, Leo asked everyone to remain silent until all who were coming had arrived. "We cannot take any risk at this point in time, so please whisper if you have to talk."

The briefing was swift and explicit and after Leo told the men about the plan it had become dead silent. When he ended his speech he said, "Now go to the other farm, no more than three at the time, do not lose anyone. Each of you has an obligation to the cause and to each other to stay with the plan. If anyone wants to depart on his own it cannot be allowed. One more thing. Last night we found an NSB-er amongst us. We have spotted him and arrested him. If anyone of you is an NSB-er you better come forward now if you want to stay alive. After this point there is no return and if an NSB-er attempts to betray us he will surely die. May God speed you and keep you safe. See you at the slaughterhouse."

If the Nazis had flown over the fields that night in the South of Holland they would have seen a pathway formed of trampled grass, where two hundred or more feet had created a trail going to the dedicated farm to load up the militant farmers.

The drivers of the two loaded trucks with stolen livestock which arrived at the slaughterhouse that night just blinked their headlights. The guards pressed a button and the automatic gates began to roll back. Once inside the gate the trucks were unloaded. The animals followed a ramp which brought them to a corral which had a high fence around it. Several openings in the corral would lead the animals to certain death.

Two hours after the trucks had entered the corral of the slaughterhouse, two more trucks blinked their lights in front of the gates. Once again the guards pressed the button and when the gates opened they drove to the entrance of the corral. The guards did not know any better. The password of the truck drivers was to blink three times; blinking meant another load of cattle was being brought in.

The minute the trucks came to a stop at the corral all the lights went out in the entire complex. It had happened before so the guards did not take any action, nor did the slaughterhouse managing operator, because so many times the lights would come back on two minutes later.

The noise of unloading cattle from the latest arriving trucks was normal too, so no one paid any attention to what was happening in the corral. The farmers had come out of the trucks and since they had been told where to take their position each group of four went silently inside the facility. This time it took a long six minutes for the lights to come back on. That was plenty of time to get about 100 farmers and twenty Boxers into position.

When the lights came on, all hell broke loose. The farmers began to shoot at anything that moved. There were perhaps only ten German soldiers inside the plant, and some thirty civilian butchers, who were all dressed in white coats, blooded from the slaughter. They were commanded to raise their arms. Those who did not do so were shot without further warning. The cattle which were still alive were next. Within a few minutes there was nothing alive in the slaughterhouse, except eight workers who had raised their hands.

The German soldiers who had been playing cards and drinking Dutch beer in the barracks outside the compound did not come into action until all had become silent; too silent for an operating facility.

When the commander of the platoon went to check on the neighboring facility, he, too, was shot, but that gunshot was the triggering sign for the rest of the soldiers to pick up their guns and run outside. They were welcomed with bullets coming their way. Not many of them were able to reach the slaughterhouse. A sergeant who had been on the toilet when the soldiers had run outside, looked through the small window and saw that his fellow soldiers were all being hit and falling. Still raising his pants, he ran to the only field phone, dialed a number and began to scream. There was no answer because the lines had been cut. The sergeant ran back to the toilet and locked himself in.

A dead silence fell over the slaughterhouse. Leo blew a whistle in one long burst and all the farmers came running towards the waiting trucks. In one minute the trucks were loaded and on their way to the exit. The guards at the gate had already been shot when they had run out of their guardhouse to see what was happening at the plant.

The first truck rammed the gates which were no match for the approaching heavy truck. The barbed wire, together with the chain link gate and the boom all flew to both sides and the truck smashed it all under its heavy wheels. The second truck followed closely and both of them disappeared in the dark night.

The first thing the Boxers had done when they had arrived at the slaughterhouse while it was still in the dark was to plant five explosive devices at strategic points inside. That resulted in a series of explosions which began when they were two kilometers away. In five minutes the entire slaughterhouse was up in flames. The stench which filled the entire city could be smelled for days. The firefighters who were not inundated with Nazis or NSB-ers took their sweet time to quench the fire. They made sure the building burned completely to the ground.

Leo had a friend who was the fire chief of the nearest fire station. He had paid him a visit the night before. "Make sure not to come too fast when you get a fire alarm from the slaughterhouse tomorrow night. I estimate around nine thirty," he had told is friend, "and tell your men to go slow in fighting the fire. This building has to be destroyed. Our farmers will be ruined if we don't succeed."

The biggest barbecue became the solution for the farmers to stay in business and the Nazis got the hint. Although a large group of Gestapo detectives was sent from Germany to find the culprits of the attack, they never did. The Nazi leadership was furious about the attack, but this time they did not blame the Resistance; instead they blamed the newly sent army, who had been too cruel in their execution of the order to loot the farms.

When Leo had dropped off the farmers in the middle of the fields, they had to find their separate ways to their farms. The two trucks disappeared in the large barn at the farm. They would stay there for a few weeks. The German license plates were removed and they would later be exchanged for plates which were taken from similar trucks at the airport. It would lead the Gestapo detectives on a wild goose chase in case someone had jotted down the numbers.

The group of Boxers each went their separate way on bicycles. That evening they would all meet at the "office" for a final briefing of the event. Leo went straight to the office; he had some people to deal with before he could go home and take a nap.

The two men in the shower/ jail cell had been eating well and both were anxious to get out and go home. When Leo released the employee from the slaughterhouse he told him to go home and see if he could find another job. "Your place of work had been terminated."

"What do you mean, terminated?" the man asked Leo.

"They had an incident there last night and the entire slaughterhouse burned down." The man could not believe his ears and began to raise several questions. "Sorry," Leo said, "that is all I can tell you, but let me give you a word of caution – don't go near the place because it will be swarming with the Gestapo and if they find out you worked there, you will be arrested and interrogated, perhaps even tortured. You are fortunate to be alive. Take my warning, go home, relax and forget you were ever here."

Before Leo took the man outside, he had him blindfolded, turned around several times, and by means of a different way, other than the normal entrance, he was guided on his way to freedom. The school building had been quite large and it was bordered by a church in which, at one time, the students of the school had been holding their church services.

Once inside the church no one was ever able to find the way back to the "office". Leo never saw the man again. He went back outside a few minutes later. There was no sign of the man. Slowly, as if he were just having a stroll, he walked back to the entrance of the "office." There was another problem he had to deal with before he could go home.

Nico van Ginkel was taken out of the other shower/jail cell. This time Leo had two fellow Boxers assisting him. The man's pockets had been thoroughly emptied the day before. What they had found did not surprise them one bit. Several ID's were in his pockets and one of them showed he was an NSB-er. It proved what Leo had suspected when he had noticed his behavior and his elaborate questioning at the meeting.

The man denied every allegation of being an NSB-er; they had no other evidence than the ID so when they asked him for references he gave them a number of names. After ten minutes of getting nowhere, the man was put back in his jail cell. "We will have to check him out more thoroughly because I just feel he is a threat to us," Leo remarked after the man had been locked up again. Leo had his connections and before he went home he stopped by a policeman who was working for the Nazis. The man was a valuable agent for the Boxers. He was able to obtain information about anyone through his commander who was also working for the Resistance.

Exhausted from two days of intensive action Leo came home that day. His wife told him the news that the slaughterhouse had been attacked and burned down and that a large detachment of Gestapo Detectives was on their way to investigate the attack. "You don't know anything about that, do you?" She asked when she gave him a well meaning hug. Leo did not answer and thought, *it's better if she knows nothing, just in case.*

Chapter Nineteen

WHAT TO DO ABOUT THE HUNGER

—~~—

Kees had stayed in Oud Beierland for two days. On the first evening of his stay he had asked the local Resistance if they had heard anything about an attack in The Hague. Nothing was known about it in the country.

He had been able to gather a nice load of food and had to find ways of transporting it to the city. There was an undertaker in the small town that did not have very much to do. He was a friend of Kees' brother. Dirk had recommended him highly. "He is a true patriot and he is willing to help anytime if it is for the Resistance."

Dirk had gone with him to introduce him to the undertaker. After a few common courtesies Kees had asked, "Is there any way you could bring a load of food to the City of The Hague tomorrow without being searched? Is it possible to hide it in a coffin, and could you possibly get travel papers to do the transport?" They came to an agreement and later that evening they loaded a coffin full of food onto the funeral carriage, in the stable of the undertaker. He had acquired the necessary papers from the local doctor clad with a counterfeit Nazi stamp on it. At seven in the morning the undertaker went on his way.

Kees and Cornelius had taken some sandwiches and left an hour later. They were happy to be on their way again and at the first roadblock, both Kees and his son were laughing in silence as they were searched. There was nothing to find on this mission. The fact that a big load had already passed the blockade was the best secret they were taking to "The Hungry City." They did not know how bad it was going to be with the food supply in the weeks and months to come.

In the city of The Hague, people were becoming desperate for food. As a result long lines of citizens could be seen walking the roads into the country. Anything that was edible was purchased, traded or bartered. The biggest problem was finding food for the hidden Jews, the now 50,000 people who would face certain death if they were captured. During the beginning of the "hunger winter," from November until the end of January, the number of hidden Jews was coming down to a minimum in the big cities. The Resistance had worked day and night to move the Jewish fugitives to farms in the country. Kees was working many nights just guiding one person at the time on foot towards a farm, sometimes fifty kilometers away from The Hague.

A curfew was still in effect, but the Nazis were scared to be on the streets at night. They only dared to go on patrols in groups of six soldiers, and then they would still only walk the main streets. The street lights had long burned out and the houses did not have electricity. If citizens would dare to keep their curtains open and a candle light would shine out, the soldiers would knock on the windows to have them close the curtains. They were all afraid because the Allied Armies were well on their way into France.

Despite the fact that all the radios had been confiscated from the people, many either still had one, or made one from parts they had kept earlier. Listening to a radio was considered a crime, punishable with jail time. But the clever Dutch had found many ways to receive the latest news from Radio Oranje, the official channel transmitted by the government of the Netherlands which was exiled to London.

Daily, at certain set times, the transmittance would come on and announce the advancement of the offensive armies. Daily, hope was received when the jingle of Radio Oranje sounded deep down in basements and in the bombed buildings all throughout The Netherlands.

Incredibly the messages of hope stilled the gnawing hunger in many. As the streets were full of people the message of hope was continually shared, but the lonely people, those who had lost loved ones, often could not muster up the hope and the hunger would win. The Nazis did one thing which worked against them but which served a purpose for the nasty NSB-ers. They made the feared traitors into teams which were used to pick up the dead bodies from the streets.

At first, Cornelius had panicked when he had seen a dead person in the street where they lived. He had come running towards the house screaming, "Mamma, Mamma, there is a man fallen down on the street and he is not getting up or moving, please come and help." Johanna had seen the destructive results of starvation several times before, and she knew the man was dead even before Cornelius took her to the scene. People were standing around the dead body trying to guess who it was that had died, when the truck with NSB-ers appeared. Roughly they picked up the body and threw it onto the truck in which several other unfortunates had been dumped earlier. It was clear that the traitors began to hate their role in the war. Many of them disappeared during the last few month of the war.

Hunger took its toll daily. At first one person here and there, then one per street; every day someone lost their life to the ever present hunger. Churches began to cook soups out of meager leftovers and rarely, but sometimes, supplies came from still existing charities.

Every one tried to cope with the gnawing hunger and the farmers closest to the city often did more than they could afford. Meat and bread were at a premium after the slaughterhouse attack. The Nazis never resumed their looting of the farms because of the price they had paid in losing so many men in the attack.

When Kees and Cornelius came home from their trip to Kees' birthplace, they were triumphant and elated. The hearse with the coffin of food was to arrive late that night. The undertaker had taken the country roads to come to the city because he would hardly ever be stopped on those roads; meanwhile he acted as though he had a local funeral to reach.

Kees had planned to have him arrive with his precious load after dark so he could unload the coffin into the Groenendijk warehouse without much suspicion. The NSB-ers were still active in the street and anything out of the ordinary would be reported in minutes to the Nazis. At night however, the Nazis did not dare to come out unless it was for an extremely important occasion.

At just after nine in the evening, the undertaker arrived, the doors of the Groenendijk warehouse were quickly opened and the entire horse and carriage went inside. With all the man power they could muster, the food was taken out of the coffin and taken downstairs into the hiding place.

There were only five Jews left that time at the van Rijn residence, so there was room for the whole stash of food. The work had to be done very quickly because Kees feared a visit from the Gestapo who was undoubtedly warned by the NSB-ers; they had never grown tired of reporting on Kees. In their heart they knew Kees was up to something and they knew he was involved in the Resistance. To their chagrin they had never been able to have Kees caught by the Gestapo. They expected a big reward if that would happen, and they were even told as much, by the Nazis.

When the rattling and banging on the double doors of the warehouse began, only the undertaker was in the warehouse. The bench was rolled and locked back in its usual place. The empty coffin was on the hearse and the horse was eating hay as if nothing had happened. The undertaker had taken a chair which Kees had provided.

The Nazis barged into the warehouse with twelve armed men. They took the undertaker and handcuffed him, pushing him back into the chair while the other soldiers searched the warehouse. The Sergeant in charge was a young punk who had grown up in the Hitler Juegent. When he had received the order to go to Holland he had seen medals, honor and promotions in his future. He would do anything to get what he himself felt he deserved for serving the Fuehrer so fervently.

This was his chance for a breakthrough; his determination to catch the Dutch in the act of sabotage was so great that he expected nothing but machine guns and hand grenades in the coffin. He commanded the undertaker to open the lid. The man looked sheepishly at the sergeant and pointed to the handcuffs he had on him. "And how do you expect me to do that sir, with these handcuffs on? Why don't you do it yourself?" He had said too much.

The Sergeant slapped him in the face. An eighteen year old Nazi punk slapping a forty five year old experienced Dutchman, a hardened man who had seen too many dead bodies! It was too much!

He jumped up from the chair and put his face right into the face of the Nazi and shouted, "You rotten Mof, don't you have any respect for your fellow man? Haven't you learned that in the Hitler Juegent?" The sergeant turned red in the face and was ready to slap him again when one of the soldiers called his name. "Herrn Oberst, please come and look at this. The sergeant was so wound up with his expectations of finding the armored treasure that he ran over to the coffin … to see… nothing.

Then he became even angrier, returning to the undertaker he was getting himself ready to break the man's neck. But something changed his mind quickly. The sergeant had not seen the Gestapo Captain enter the building. He was quietly talking to the undertaker. The sergeant had to restrain himself from the intentions he had on his mind with the man who was disappointing him so much.

"Why have you come here, sir?" the Captain asked. The undertaker saw the change in attitude in this Captain in comparison to the Sergeant's attitude. So he grabbed onto the opportunity and answered the Captain:

"I just arranged with the owner of this warehouse to spend the night here because tomorrow morning I have to pick up the body of a citizen from my home town and bring it to a cemetery in Oud Beierland. I cannot leave my horse outside overnight, and as you can see, I am ready to do my job as usual, having brought an empty coffin with me."

The Captain dismissed the soldier who was holding the undertaker by his arm and commanded the Sergeant to unlock the handcuffs on the man. "I need to know who reported this incident; I am getting sick and tired of these useless reports. We are wasting our time. Sergeant, go get the fink who reported this, now!" Minutes later the NSB-er was brought in. "What is your name, sir?" the Captain asked."

"My name is Art Schimmel, and yes, I reported this situation as being very unusual for a horse drawn hearse, with a coffin parking in Mr. Groenendijk's warehouse. What is the reward I'll be getting Captain, sir?"

The Captain did not answer him, instead he commanded the sergeant to handcuff the man and take him to the Gestapo office. Then he said to the protesting traitor, "We will determine your reward when we get there." He barked a final command and within minutes the warehouse was empty, the undertaker was left by himself and the doors were safely closed behind them.

Two minutes later the work bench began to move. Kees stuck his head above the table and said, "Come, my friend, my wife has prepared some great onion soup for us. Come on through here and we'll chat a bit before we turn in. By the way, we do have a bed for you inside the house, so you don't have to sleep in the coffin."

"Very funny, thank you," the man answered with a grim smile.

Cornelius welcomed the undertaker and wanted to show him his little farm in the back yard but his mother said, "Cornelius, not now, the man is tired and hungry, besides it is dark outside. Why don't you do that tomorrow morning?"

There was a knock on the front door, a very moderate knock. It was too soft to be from the Nazis. Kees went to look through the window to see who it was and to determine if he should open the door. He saw Leo across the street, standing in the shade. Leo, who was lighting a cigarette!

It was the usual sign for Kees to go outside to talk with him. He had just walked past the door and invisibly made his knock, as always, they did this inconspicuously, so that no one would be compromised.

A few minutes later Kees walked outside, turned right and walked to the end of the street. There he made another right turn. Leo had seen him leave and walked out of the shadow to the left and then took a left turn. After a brief moment the two met each other and stepped into a portico, one which had been left standing while the rest of the house had collapsed under a bomb which had made a direct hit on the building.

Leo began, "What I need to know is how is it possible that an NSB-er was among the farmers at your meeting before you came to meet with us. I also want to warn you in case the guy has spoken to someone the day after your meeting. He came to me after the second meeting and foolishly asked too many questions. I sensed immediately that he was a traitor and I need to make you aware of the possibility that he could have compromised you."

"What have you done with him?" Kees inquired.

"We have taken him to the 'office' and will keep him there until we have ample proof that he is indeed an NSB-er. Now that we have the proof I want to ask you if you can arrange to get him to the prison farm, you know, the one where we keep so many of them."

Kees nodded, "Yes, of course I can arrange that. I am glad you caught him. At least the Nazis would not have him to testify against me when he has disappeared. I will arrange it tonight, in order not to waste any time or take any risk. The people at the airport will take him as they have done with dozens of them already. Have him ready and wrapped for delivery by eight tomorrow morning. And thanks for your concern for me. The slaughterhouse was a good one, wasn't it?"

"The Nazis don't even know where to begin to look. We had it sewed up clean and neat," Leo answered him proudly.

Kees walked home briskly, he had to get his bicycle and get to the airport quickly. The men usually left at ten o'clock. It was nine thirty when he hopped on his bike.

The way Kees went to the hangar at the airport was dark and without any soldiers. Just west of the Hoornbrug, the only bridge he had to cross to the airport, he had a friend who was a ferry operator. He lived on the edge of the river and his boat was always ready for the Resistance. He had a rope which sunk down into the water going across the river, by which he pulled the small ferry. It was more like a row boat and it was only used at night.

Further down the river the man owned and operated a real ferry boat which could take as many as twenty people at one time. The little ferry had been a real treasure for the Resistance. It was the only secure way to the important hangar at the airport and they all knew about it, except the Nazis.

Herman the ferry operator was a greengrocer as well. Before the war he operated his store right around the corner from Kees's house. But when the supply dried up he had begun the ferry business. Herman de Vriend was a true Christian. Before the war Kees had attended his Saturday night sing-alongs with the accompaniment of the old organ. They had Bible studies and there was nothing else Kees would have rather done on Saturday nights. The war had messed up the schedule, but Kees hoped they could soon start those evenings up again.

The Allied armies were getting closer and Herman was all wound up about a pending liberation. "I hope there will be enough people still alive because the food supply is getting very low," Kees remarked while he was pulled across the river.

"Are you coming back soon?" Herman asked, "I will be ready for you, and all you have to do is pull this thin rope here next to the big one. It will sound a little bell inside my house and I will be right there. Make sure to lay your bike down in the grass and stay flat yourself too, until I come." With that advice Kees had landed on the other side of the river and quickly crossed the road into the fields again.

There was a stream around the airport and where the hangar was located. The creek was too wide to jump across. The men of the Resistance who operated the self-made ambulances had made a little raft to go across. No Nazi had ever seen it because it was tied in between the reeds and with one push it would bring one person at the time to the hangar. A small door close to the crossing had been cut in the steel corrugated wall. The sound of three knocks, two short and one long, was the way to have it opened from the inside. Kees was finished in minutes and returned the same way he had come. One more traitor would be taken out of circulation the next day.

Chapter Twenty

HOPE KEEPS PEOPLE ALIVE

The back yard of the city house was a refuge for Cornelius. It had become his pride and joy, but also that of his parents who showed it to every visitor, telling them how much produce it had yielded. The Jewish guests under the floor of the house were very happy with the garlic Cornelius grew, but in particular the fresh lettuce and collard greens. They were a godsend in a time when nothing was for sale.

Cornelius took constant lessons from Marie at the Brandwijk farm in growing, sowing and reaping and in particular the planning which went into growing new crops. In the late fall planting vegetables was not possible because of the coming winter. Yet Cornelius had learned that he could prepare new young plants in his little greenhouse that he himself had constructed out of old windows from the bombed ruins in the neighborhood. He had also learned how he could make a hotbed. It was hard work for the little boy who was smaller than the spade he was using, to dig a hole three yards long, and four feet wide, and digging it two feet deep, in order to fill the hotbed with layers of straw and horse manure.

Cornelius had made a cart out of an old wooden crate fastening it on top of an old baby carriage. This way he would haul a lot of manure and old straw to his back yard farm to fill the new hotbed. His mother protested strongly when he would pull the cart with manure through the narrow hallway of the house.

He had learned to cover the straw and horse manure with a foot of plain straw, thus he was able to plant lettuce, spinach and cucumbers in December and begin harvesting in January. Kees was amazed about his son's knowledge and motivation to make his farm productive. After the war ended, Johanna proudly remarked, "The back yard garden saved our lives."

The stable of an undertaker was close to his house. The funeral business had been taken over by the brother of the previous undertaker, who had died in the process of taking Jews to a farm in the province of Zeeland. The brother was helping the Resistance even more frequently than his deceased brother had. With the help of the Resistance he had found a way to deceive the Nazis' search dogs which had discovered his brother.

It was on a cold November day when Cornelius went to the undertaker's stable. He had loaded up his little self-made trailer and came out of the stable pulling it with all his might, when a German patrol passed him. The soldiers made a remark to each other, "Why is this boy hauling manure?" They decided to follow him and see where he was going. Cornelius soon noticed that the soldiers were watching him. His instincts told him to mislead them as he had done so many times when he was on trips with his father.

When he reached his home he passed by the windows as close as he could. His mother was always in the front room, so he did not look into the house, hoping she would see him being followed by a band of Nazis. He then passed by and went to the Brook Sloot. It was a creek which ran near his house. He noticed that the soldiers were still following him. When he reached the rose beds which were along the creek he stopped.

He had walked faster than he realized and had to catch his breath when he stopped. The soldiers had almost stumbled into him when he had stopped and when he began to shovel the manure around the roses they laughed and went on. *Good for you, you nasty people*, Cornelius thought, *good for you to waste your time following a small boy to see if you can accuse his parents of something.*

When the soldiers were out of sight, he did the same as his father would have done any time they had a run-in with soldiers. He breathed a sigh of relief and said, "That was a close call. Thank you, Lord."

He did not shovel the entire load on the rose beds, but walked the short distance back to his home. Johanna came running to the door when she saw him coming. "Cornelius what on earth were you thinking, having soldiers chasing you? I was getting so worried when I saw you walking by with all the Moffen behind you, what happened?"

"Nothing happened, Mom. I just did not want them to come here and trample my garden, so I acted as if I was fertilizing the rose beds on the side of the creek. When I started that, they left. I fooled them didn't I?" He smiled with a big smile.

Johanna complimented him on his smart move, "One day you will become a great Resistance man, Cornelius. I am proud of you."

He pulled what was left of his load through the narrow hallway under protest of his mother and began to shovel the straw and horse manure into the hole he had dug. Johanna came to see what he was doing and asked, "Why are you putting all that stuff so deep down in that hole you dug?"

"We call that a hotbed Mom," he remarked, too wise for his age. "I need to get at least one more load and then I will press it together before I put the soil on top of it. After that I am going to place some glass windows over it and then I can sow the seeds Marie has given me – spinach, lettuce and cucumbers. We will be able to eat those in January when nothing grows outside."

His mother had to brush the tears away which were welling up in her eyes. This child was smarter than any child at that age should be. His determination to make it through this "hunger winter" was astonishing. "Incredible job, Cornelius," was all she could say while hiding her tears.

Cornelius went to get two more loads and after a few hours he came back inside and went to his mother, "It's all done, Mom. You can sleep easy from now on because we will have food on the table this winter."

The next day, Kees and Cornelius had to go to the Brandwijk farm, because four Jewish people had been chosen to go to Switzerland. Kees had to arrange for the transport by ambulance and for the counterfeit ID's which had been prepared by the printer. He had to take a camera to take pictures of the people and then bring them back to the farm a few hours later. Cornelius was very excited because he had the chance to stay with Marie with whom he was very much in love. He had a dozen questions for her and she gave him all the time he needed to teach him about growing and planting.

This time his main concern was how he would be able to have lots and lots of marigolds on whatever day the liberation would come. He was excited to tell her about the hotbed he had created and what he had sown in it. He did have a few questions about watering the hotbed. He wanted to know if and when he should open the windows of the hotbed.

After their arrival each one, father and son, went their separate ways. Kees went to the Jews' hiding place, and Cornelius went to find his "hero" girl friend. He found her way back in the fields where she was collecting dandelions for the rabbits and the chickens. When she saw him coming she felt the joy of teaching the young boy and the love he had for her in the way he hugged her.

"Here comes my best student and my favorite friend," she shouted from afar, "Cornelius, I am so happy to see you. Come here, my boy."

Cornelius replied enthusiastically, "Marie, I have lots to ask you. Please come to the farm where we can sit in the hay. I have been waiting to come and tell you what I have done in my garden." They walked while talking up a storm on the long way back through the green meadows full of dandelions. There were not enough cows left to eat them. The hours went by quickly when the two were together. Cornelius had not even felt the hunger that reigned in his tiny body.

Kees had seen the four people who were going to be transported the next day. He had taken their pictures and had gone back to the city. "How would you like to stay here for the night Cornelius?" Marie had asked him. "Then I can tell you a lot about what to do at your little farm in the city. You know something? I know where there is a duck nesting with a dozen eggs. Let's go and get you some." But first they went to eat the big slices of bread which Mrs. Brandwijk had baked herself, with ham and lots of butter. *If I did not have to help my dad with his distribution of food stamps I could live on this farm and marry Marie,* Cornelius thought to himself.

Normally, it took Kees more than three hours to come back from the printer in the city. He was carrying the fake ID's on his body and thought what a great set up they had when Cornelius was with him. The boy was the perfect carrier and decoy, the Nazis had never, ever touched him. This time he was taking a great risk riding around with four fake documents. He decided to watch for and avoid all road blocks as much as he could. He also planned to throw the counterfeit ID's in a ditch, if he had to.

He stopped his bike and sat down in the tall grass along the river de Vliet to make up his mind about his security measures when a Nazi motorcycle with two soldiers on it was approaching in the distance. Quickly he pulled the ID's together and wrapped them in his black handkerchief. He shoved the package under the bushes and lay down in the grass.

He heard the solders talk above the sound of the engine and when it came closer he heard that the engine was slowing down. They had seen him and they were stopping. Oh Lord, please protect me, he prayed. Kees stood up when the motorcycle had stopped next to him on the road.

One of the soldiers called out, "Ausweiss." Kees began to fumble in his pockets to find the needed document. "Schnell," the other soldier screamed as he walked towards Kees. He kicked Kees and pushed him to the ground. Then both of them began to kick and hit him. One blow and then another was hitting his face, and then another and more kicking. Then total darkness fell over him.

They briefly looked through his pockets and found his wallet with his Ausweiss; they pocketed the money he had on him and left him for dead in the grassy ditch. Then they left, laughing …

A farmer who saw Kees lying in the ditch an hour or so later stopped, he threw his bike down in the grass and thought to himself, *another victim of the raging hunger, you could almost say, one of the lucky ones to leave this horrible war.* He looked closer to see if he could recognize the man.

Slowly, Kees moved and groaned as he woke up. The farmer was startled at first, but then he helped Kees to sit up and asked, "What happened to you, sir?" Kees tried to talk, but the words he uttered were muted by a stream of blood coming out of his mouth. *I have some water in my bag,* the farmer thought, *perhaps he can wash the blood out of his mouth and speak.*

It worked. Minutes later Kees had recovered his composure and told the farmer what had happened. "Those rotten soldiers think it is fun to beat someone up; even their commanders tolerate this kind of behavior. This new batch of soldiers is ruthless and the Allieds better hurry up and make an end to this nasty war. Would you be able to get up and ride your bicycle? If you can, my farm is only half a kilometer further and there my wife can fix you up."

Kees tried to get up; it seemed difficult at first but then he thought of Jesus, how he had fallen down on the road to his crucifixion, while he was carrying his heavy cross. In Matthew He said, "For my yoke is easy and My burden is light." With that thought and the words of Jesus in his heart, he received instant power to get up and ride his bike alongside the farmer, to his house.

The farm was right next door to the Brandwijk farm; Kees did not say much. The lady cleaned up his blood stains and washed off some of the blood from his clothes. A cup of soup gave him strength. He was bruised all over his body but as far as he could feel, nothing was broken inside his body.

An hour later he thanked the farmer and his wife and left. He did not tell them that he was going to their neighbors. During this time it was not wise to volunteer information to anyone. So, he arrived two hours later than he had planned to get back to the Brandwijk farm. He decided, then and there, never to go on a trip without Cornelius again. He had never thought of the necessity of having his son as a decoy, to be a deterrent for the Nazis. Later he realized how greatly it worked when Cornelius was on the back of his bicycle.

They sat down in the upper room and Brandwijk asked him why it had taken him more than three hours to come back and why he was all bruised and bloody. When he told his story about the events of the last two hours they shook their heads. The Brandwijks had had their experience with the Nazis too. They had lost their son to this war and more than half of their livestock. They were living in constant fear for having a large group of Jews beneath their haystack, and they were under continual pressure about how to feed all those hungry stomachs.

Kees stood up and swayed a little before he went to the stable where the four blessed Jews had been waiting for their final papers to freedom. Suddenly he realized he did not have the new ID's. He had left them in the bushes where the altercation had occurred.

He would have to go back and get them, this time he would take Cornelius. It was becoming too risky without his decoy. Kees asked where he could find his son. "You sit down Kees; I will get him for you," the farmer told him. "You may think you are strong, but with what I can see, you are still not up to par. Perhaps you should wait a couple of hours to get back on that blessed bike of yours."

Cornelius could not be found anyway because he was far away in the fields. Marie had taken him to the river which ran along the meadows in search of duck nests with eggs in them. They had found several nests, most of them without eggs. Marie did not tell him, but this was the wrong time of the year, even though ducks can lay eggs at any time.

Then the triumphant voice of Cornelius echoed over the green and silent meadows, his voice sounding hollow and far through the fields. "I found them, twelve of them, come and see Marie! I want to take ten of them like last time; Then I might get six ducks to hatch and have duck meat for Easter. Cornelius was talking too loud; his voice could be heard for miles. But it helped Brandwijk to find the two.

Marie had carefully picked up the eggs out of the nest and gathered them in her apron. Carefully she walked towards her father and showed him their find. "Cornelius," he said "you will become the farmer of the year and after this war is over and you have grown up, I want you to come and work for me here at the farm. You'll make a great farmer." Chatting all the way back to the farm, the threesome enjoyed the crisp fall weather. The war, for that moment, was far away and the worries which would consume them every hour of the day would have to wait until later.

When Kees saw his son, being so carefree and without worry, a great feeling of thankfulness filled his mind. God is good, he reminded himself and I should be grateful that none of my family has been lost in this war. Grateful that he was able to care for so many people, to save their lives and that provision had always been made without much effort, was enough to fill him with joy. He felt great strength coming over him and decided not to dwell on the recent event, but to forgive and do what he had to do.

It took the two on their bicycle half an hour to find the ID's under the bushes and get them to the waiting and delighted Jews at the stable. Instructions were given to be ready at six a.m. the next morning. The arriving ambulance would be parked in the stable that evening under cover of darkness. The Brandwijks had sectioned off a place where the ambulance could park and it would be covered with hay. Just in case inquisitive Nazis would follow the ambulance to the farm, one of the Jews would be ready, dressed as a German soldier and bandaged up like a mummy. No precaution was left undone to preserve the use of the ambulances.

It had grown late by the time Kees and Cornelius left the farm. The duck eggs were securely placed in the seat beneath Cornelius and some more food was packed in the side bags. Cornelius had two small cooked chickens under his jacket which made him look like a fat little boy. Kees would have to hurry to beat the coming curfew. In particular, riding in the country, he would be at risk of being caught by the traveling soldiers who seemed to take joy in arresting innocent citizens who were caught by the pending hour of the curfew.

Kees knew he could make it on time as long as he was not stopped too many times on his trip. He was glad to have his son behind him. Their act was always the best way to shorten the stops at the blockades.

This time they made it without hitting any roadblocks; the Nazis must have been busy elsewhere. The door opened in the Deiman Straat and for one night there was peace inside the house. Johanna wanted to hear all about their trip and she nourished the two with her love. "I know how important it is to take Cornelius with me on every trip. This thing would have never happened if he would have been with me. Who would have thought that a little guy like him could have such great protective power against the Nazi thugs?"

Chapter Twenty One

UNWILLINGNESS TO HELP JEWS

In the city of Arnhem there were practically only German military left. They were living in the nicest houses which had been spared by the fighting and bombing of the Canadians and which had been duly confiscated by the Nazis.

When the Canadians had landed, the Nazis had commanded all citizens to evacuate the city of Arnhem. One huge stream of miserable people had left the city. They could not take much with them on their evacuation. In most cases they just carried a gunnysack or a small suitcase. They had swarmed the country side in every direction to find a roof to sleep under and to find something to eat. On their sad way, many people had helped the fugitives. Farmers had allowed them to sleep in their hay lofts and had shared their meager food supply.

Some brave people had decided to stay in the beleaguered city. They were people from all of walks of life. There were also people who could not walk, or elderly who did not care if they died after so many years of lack and threats. There were people who thought to take advantage of the emptied-out city; they were the thieves and the prostitutes who saw great business opportunities with the German soldiers. There were Jews who did not dare to go into the streets, and there were fugitives, collaborators and even German deserters.

Two days after the order had come to evacuate the city, the Germans began to take possession of the nicest homes, trampling the Persian carpets with their army boots and sleeping in the beds where once families had slept in peace. When the fighting began, the Canadians launched all kinds of attacks on the city and the Nazis made barricades from anything they could find. Homes were bombed. Churches and public buildings collapsed under the heavy fire from the Canadian cannons, their mortars and grenades.

In the midst of all the noise of war, two people had moved from house to house to find a safe place to stay. What looked like an everyday Dutch couple was actually a pair of Jews who had decided not to listen to the Jewish Council. They had not accepted any help from the Resistance. They had sold their furniture store when rumors of the war had begun; as far back as one year before the Nazis had attacked The Netherlands.

They had never given any thought about the anti-Semitic propaganda. They were Jewish by birth but did not follow the Jewish laws and rituals. The only thing that had divulged their identity was their Jewish name. Lucas and Ruth Schmall had sold their store for a handsome sum of money. They had never deposited their proceeds in a bank account. They had hidden their funds in a graveyard and only they knew how to find it each time they needed money. When the war had begun and the transportations of Jews had increased in both number and frequency, they were virtually non-existent. They were not registered at any city hall because just weeks before the Nazis had intruded the country they had gone to the city administration and told them they were leaving the country. The city clerk had duly removed them from the records.

They never left the country; together they had decided to stay put in their small house in the center of Arnhem. Then a bomb hit their house. They had been out walking along the river when the center of Arnhem was hit. They had feared for the worst and their fears had been justified when they came closer to their house. There was not much value in what they had lost, and they just left the bomb site and received temporary shelter from the Red Cross. Two weeks later the fighting had stopped and the country had surrendered. The Schmalls found an abandoned house in the center of old Arnhem and settled down in their new dwelling. "We will ride this war out here," they had said to each other, and went on living their lonely life style.

But the fighting had never stopped! The beleaguered city of Arnhem was severely damaged and when the Canadians had landed in September of 1944, it became the center of warfare once more. The fugitives moved deeper and deeper into the ruins and finally ended up in the basement of the old city hall, which had been hit by a barrage of bombs and mortars during the Canadian offensive. Their daily activities of finding food and avoiding the German patrols had become their greatest task.

Lucas and Ruth were only in their early thirties, but they had made themselves look very old when they went out on the streets. Dressed in old rags, their faces made dirty with charcoal, moving slowly, heavily, and bent over, they were seen by the Nazis as seventy year olds. When the patrols passed them, they would look in pity at the old shuffling couple and never bothered them. Yet, they felt the threat of everyday life in the ruined city and feared more for their lives every day as time went on. One day a young farmhand on a bicycle, at least that was what he looked like, stopped the couple and asked them if they needed his help. The casual meeting became one they would never forget!

The man who had accosted them was the now self-proclaimed Dominee Henk de Groot, who had visited a group of hidden Jews in the city and ministered to them about his new found faith. He was busy with his visits all over the country but he never passed up an opportunity to help others.

The old couple was surprised to hear the man speak to them. Usually people avoided them for fear of contagious diseases which ran so rampant during the latter end of the war. When the man looked them in the eyes he saw more than what they appeared to be. Henk decided right then that these people needed help immediately, because he felt the great danger they were in had not dawned upon them yet.

"Can we go and talk somewhere where it is safe? I think I can help you," Henk asked them softly.

The two looked at each other and the man nodded his head very lightly saying, "Yes, we can go to a building just behind us. I know the way into the basement, please follow us." His voice sounded much younger than he looked and Henk decided to get the truth out of them so he would be able to assist them to a better living situation.

The ruin they entered must have been one of the first buildings which was bombed. Grass was growing in between the rubble and as they climbed through the concrete and broken windows Henk noticed that there was not one piece of wood left. Apparently it had all been taken by the people in search of fuel for their stoves. They had to climb through a concrete arch which had remained standing and, at last, came to a concrete staircase which led to the former basement.

The couple sat down on an old sofa which seemed to be used regularly, because it was not covered with dust like all the other furniture in the place. Henk asked them, "Do you live here in this dumpy hide out?"

They nodded their heads simultaneously, "No, we have a much better place a little ways from here but here we can talk as you wished."

The man looked at Henk expectantly and when Henk opened his mouth and said, "Shabbat shalom," he noticed a flickering in their eyes.

One had to be very careful in communicating with any stranger; many a time the German Secret Police had arrested Jews in the same way Henk had acted. But when Henk dug up his original Ausweiss with the big red J on it the couple began to open up. Especially when he told them that he was perhaps the only Rabbi left in the country. He told them about his work as he had visited the hiding places and had ministered to the Jews on their Jewish holidays.

When Lucas spoke it sounded like a confession. He was emptying his heart about all the years of events and how they escaped the trip to the death camps. Even before the war had begun in Holland the two had been harassed by Dutch Jew haters. Those who sympathized with the Nazism of Hitler and those who would later become the feared NSB-ers, had been doing their gossiping and making threats. They had marked their furniture store with slogans on the windows and on the pavement in front of the store. They had been telling the neighbors that they should not buy from Jews. Gradually the customers had stopped coming in fear of the wrath of the collaborators.

A good friend of theirs had offered to buy the store from them just two months before the Germans attacked the country. They had made a good deal. They sold the store for cash and moved downtown to the city of Arnhem where they were able to rent a small apartment.

They had hidden their money in the grave of Ruth's mother and they would draw from their stash in small amounts. Lucas would be the watchman when they needed money while Ruth was on her knees at the grave. They had a special time to make their draws; it was always half an hour after midnight. No one had ever suspected the two, and no one had ever followed them to the cemetery.

Henk had been listening without interrupting Lucas and after a good hour and what seemed a life time for the couple, he asked a question, "As the war draws to an end do you still feel safe here; don't you think you should get out of here? Because soon – very,very soon – all hell will break loose. The armies are going to fight their final battle, and because Arnhem is supposed to be an empty city with only German occupants, it is going to be the center of attacks."

Then finally Henk dared to ask the question: "Do you have papers to even appear on the road without being arrested?"

They shook their heads, both at the same time. "All we have is the original Ausweiss with the red J on it. We never used it because we were not registered anywhere. We told the clerks of the city that we were getting out of the country just before it all started. In the beginning when the Nazis demanded everyone to get an Ausweiss, we thought it would be a good idea to have something. No one ever thought the Nazis would round up all the Jews and ship them off to the concentration camps. When we saw all our friends being picked up we decided to ride out the war all by ourselves, but now we are stuck here in the middle of the rubble and the upcoming battle."

Henk was silent for what seemed an eternity. He was praying silently, "Lord, what should I do with these two of your chosen people? If I take them on the streets they will be arrested in no time. If I leave them here they might perish in the upcoming battle which could start tomorrow."

When he lifted his head and broke the silence he knew what to do. He did not tell the two any of the details, but he told them he would help them as quickly as he could. "Is there a place where you are safe even when the bombs start dropping?" It seemed like a silly question, but Lucas nodded his head.

"Yes we have a safe place. It is so deep down in the ground that no one will be able to find us. It is beneath so much rubble that a bomb can hardly do any more damage."

"Very well," Henk made his decision. "I need to know where that is and how I will be able to find you. It will take me about four hours to make arrangements to bring you to temporary safety. After that it will take me a week to come back and bring you safely to The Hague. Don't ask me how, but I know what to do, trust me in this."

"If you follow us we will show you our makeshift bunker and also how you can get our attention when you return." Lucas ended the conversation with, "May God guide and protect you. Shalom, dear friend."

Henk followed the two through the rubble, stumbling over chunks of concrete. He had no idea where they were going and he was wondering how he would ever find them again after they parted. Lucas was aware of Henk's puzzling expression and remarked, "Don't worry, we will give you plenty of indications on how you can find your way back here, and by the way, I will take you back to where your bicycle is too."

When they reached their destination, Lucas pointed at a bill board, a round pillar on which the Germans pasted their nasty announcements. The pillar was lying sideways and hung partly over a section of the wall that used to surround the City Hall of Arnhem. "That pillar is the only one that is not upright in this section of the city because the Nazis don't need it here anymore for lack of readers.

"When you come down this main street you can see it very well, and when you do, you can park your bike right here behind these urinals. No one will see it. Besides hardly anyone ever comes here. Then you go over this heap of rubble and down from that is a steel door, you see?" He lifted the steel door up and a steel bar fell down and supported it at a slant. "I put that steel bar on it with an old hinge I found so we can enter and close it by kicking the bar flat."

He did so after they had entered and the steel door fell into place. It closed the entrance which led to a wide staircase which went down for at least three stories, or so it appeared.

When they finally reached the bottom they stood in front of a pond. Henk thought of the Israelites when they had left Egypt and ended up in front of the Red Sea. *What now?* He thought. Lucas bent down and felt with his hand in the water until he had a rope in his hand and began to pull on it. On the other side something began to move in the water. In the half darkness Henk could see something coming towards them. A raft made of old ten gallon Jerry cans and a door on top of it came floating towards them. "That is very clever indeed," Henk uttered in amazement. "It takes a Dutchman to beat a Nazi, is that not an expression?"

"Actually, 'It takes a Dutchman to beat a Jew' is the real expression," Lucas answered.

It took about a minute for the three to get across the pond which was nothing less than the lowest basement of the building, which at one time was actively used as the city archives.

They went up one staircase where Henk was asked to enter a most luxurious room. It was paneled all around, including the ceilings, with beautiful oak paneling.

"This used to be the private resting and conference room of the Mayor who, at one time, practically lived here." Lucas announced. "We found it by accident when there was no water in the lower basement. It was well-preserved because the small staircase was covered with rubble and no one had bothered to search any further. When Ruth and I came here for the first time we climbed up this staircase and found the door; what a surprise that was! Just a week later we came back to see if we could live here permanently after the water had filled the lower basement. We thought it was an act of God to preserve these living quarters for us. We have lived here for three years and we never saw any intruders or Nazis for that matter."

Even the furniture was well preserved in the large room. When they all sat down, Henk told them what he had on his mind. "I know people in the Resistance in The Hague who can make new papers for you, perfectly forged Ausweisses with your own pictures on them. Once I bring those, you will be picked up by a German ambulance."

The two looked at each other with a bewildered look. Henk read the fear in their eyes. "Don't worry. It is a safe German ambulance, operated by the Resistance. Then you will be brought to The Hague at a very safe shelter underneath a city home. I have known the people who live there for four years and they must have saved the lives of a thousand Jews by now."

Henk looked around the room and then he thought of the sandy floor underneath the house in the Deiman Straat. It would be a big change, but safety and preserving their lives was more important than luxury. Hopefully it would only be for few weeks. The Americans were coming, that was for sure.

No one knew there was going to be seven more months of misery.

"Please give me your Ausweisses; I will have to take them with me to use the pictures and have the correct spelling of your names, unless they sound so Jewish that we will have to change them. I definitively need the pictures," Henk told them.

Lucas reached in his pockets and produced a neatly folded handkerchief. When he unwrapped it, a small envelope made of gunnysack cloth emerged. He had to cut it open to take the two Ausweisses out. The papers were as good as new. "We put them in here just in case, and we have never taken them out, until now," Ruth explained. "At first we were mighty proud of the red J on them, but when we found out what its purpose was, we sewed them up and never intended to show them to anyone. You are the first one to see them."

Henk accepted the two documents and studied the names. He read *Lucas A Schmall.* The other one read *Ruth H.Schmall.* He wondered, w*here have I seen or heard that name before?* It took him all the way back to The Hague to find the answer to his question. He did not mention his thoughts when he left because he knew time would tell.

Then Dominee, former Rabbi Levi Strauss, aka Henk de Groot, alias Han de Clerck, Insurance salesman, alias Cor van der Weiden, farmhand, was on his way to the farm of Krelis van Houten in Oosterbeek.

He was deep in thought wondering where he had seen the name 'Schmall' before. He also tried to remember which identity he had used the last and only time he had met Krelis. He remembered that he was with Kees and that he had met a young Jewish man at the farm, who had never worn the star.

It finally dawned on him that this Krelis wanted to have nothing to do with Jews, let alone hiding them. He thought that he had used his insurance salesman name; Han de Clerck. He was not completely convinced about it and decided to play it safe and try to have Krelis guess his name. That way he would not make a mistake, especially with an anti-Jewish person.

It took him an hour and a half to get to the farm in Oosterbeek. Nestled on the estate of Baron van Boetselaer, the Krelis and Betsy's farm provided a very peaceful retreat. He thought the two Schmalls could have a free and restful time there for as long as it would take him to get back with the new ID's. The trick was to avoid any mention or hint about their Jewishness, he decided.

The two shepherd dogs came running towards him as he rode his bike towards the ancient farmhouse. It must have been built in the sixteen hundreds when the castle of the Baron had been erected. At that time the dwellings of the Barons were built in grandeur, while the farmers and workers had been housed in the smallest possible buildings. Now more than three centuries later the houses and farms on the estates had become antique and very desirable.

The dogs were running along with him to the house, barking but not threatening. They were typical farm dogs, a lot of noise but no aggression. Their barking caused the people to come outside before the visitor reached the house. Betsy was the first person to greet him when he stepped off his bicycle. She exclaimed: "If it is not the insurance salesman from The Hague, I'll be... What brings you to our peaceful dwelling place?" Henk did not answer yet because he saw the young Jewish man, with an alias he did not remember, come outside also. He saw a flicker of recognition in his eyes and remembered he had talked to the young man at length in the haystack.

Krelis came walking out with of the stable, an iron bucket in one hand and a rake in the other. He dropped both items and came to shake Henk's hand. "Well, if you think you can sell us any insurance, you have to wait until this hellish war is over and we can earn some real money again. Han de Clerck, what brings you to Oosterbeek, so far from The Hague my friend? Hunger? Or do you just need a bed for the night? Come on inside, it's too cold here in the yard, I'm sure you would like some soup. Betsy, do you have any soup left?"

He rattled on for a long time, Henk hardly said a word even though the questions kept coming he did not get a chance to answer them. When he finally stopped talking, Geert the farmhand, the 'Jew without a star', took over the conversation. His questions were more about life in the West of the country and he wanted to know how far the Allieds were in liberating the country.

Finally, after at least half an hour with a barrage of words from the hosts, Henk was able to talk. "The Tommies and the Yankees are still held up in Belgium and Luxemburg. They have entered the south of the country, but they are held up at the Rijn River. Any day now, they expect to cross over and liberate us. There are constant rumors about a large offensive on this side of the river, but the Nazis have a lot of equipment on this side which will have to be bombed before they cross over. Arnhem will be a central point and everyone expects the city to be totally flattened with bombs and shells from both sides. Luckily you are in a quiet zone with no strategically important points for battle.

"They are coming, you can count on that. When? Nobody knows. There is a huge shortage of food in the West. People are dropping dead in the streets from hunger. The new army Hitler has sent is made up with the ultimate of fanatics.

"They are the former Hitler Juegent, brainwashed brats who never fought before and who still think they can suppress the Dutch and win the war. They made some major mistakes when they first arrived and luckily the Generals have tamed them a bit. They are still fanatics and will kill anyone who is in their path." Henk paused for a minute allowing anticipation to build, some expectation of what was to come when he switched to the purpose of his visit.

"I am here to help a couple who are still living in the city of Arnhem and who need to get out of there to go to The Hague. They need a temporary shelter and I am asking you people to help me help them."

The first thing which came out of Krelis' mouth was, "They are not Jews I hope, because you know I won't take them under any circumstance. I serve the Germans here on a regular basis and make some good money at it. I can't afford to lose their business. I never liked the Jews and I am not about to change my opinion about that!"

Henk nodded his head and said, "I know where you're coming from, but these are just ordinary people, a couple who have endured the war in horrible circumstances hoping it would have ended sooner. They are at the end of their rope and in grave danger when the battle over Arnhem breaks loose. They need a peaceful place for a couple of weeks while I can make arrangements to transfer them to The Hague."

Krelis looked at Betsy who nodded her head saying,"I would like a woman here for awhile. I have not talked to another woman since the two sisters left and I don't mind a couple of visitors, as long as they are not Jewish. When will they arrive here?"

"I can go get them in the next hour and be back here in two." Henk answered them. It will be better to do it in the dark so we don't run into any patrols – you know how that can be; besides these two don't have any ID's, so we will have to make sure we stay low while bringing them here."

It was Geert's turn to say something, "Why don't we go get them with the horse and carriage? The Nazis never stop me because they all know me. We can hide them under some straw and the mission will be quick and easy." He looked expectantly at Krelis for approval.

For a minute they thought he was going to refuse, but then he said, "Oh well, yes go ahead, we might as well be good in these last days of the war."

"I'll get the horse hitched to the carriage and pile some hay on it. I'll be ready in ten minutes." He ran outside and prepared his plan.

"Would you like to stay here for the night as well?" Betsy asked Henk, "How about some more soup?" Henk agreed to the soup. His stomach was still not very full and he realized he had not eaten all day, except for the bowl of soup when he had arrived. He realized how blessed he was compared to the people in the big cities. There were thousands of people and thousands of children who had to go to bed without any food at all.

Chapter Twenty Two

A HARVEST OUT OF DESPERATION

—ꟷ—

It was a beautiful day in mid November of 1944. The city of The Hague had awakened to great news from Radio Oranje. The Allied forces had finally crossed the southern borders of The Netherlands. The cities of Breda and Tilburg had been taken without much fighting. The population was delighted, but just fifty kilometers further north the German army had dug itself in for a fierce battle.

Between the southern province of Brabant and the West of Holland were two major rivers which formed the greatest obstacle for the advancing Allied armies. In haste, bunkers and trenches had to be dug and for that the Nazis needed manpower.

The blue sky that November morning seemed promising, but it turned out to be dreadful day because as early as eight o'clock in the morning all the available trucks and soldiers went on a hunt for the needed manpower. The speed with which this hunt was carried out was like a duck hunt with machine guns.

Wherever men were found, no matter their age, no matter if they were working in a factory or whether they could prove they were already working for the war industry; they were picked up and trucked to the front lines. No one knew where they were going. No questions were answered and nothing could be brought along by the captured men. In The Hague the man hunt produced a large harvest in the first three hours of the day. More than three thousand men had been picked up, but by then the news had spread across the city and the men went into hiding or sneaked out of the city.

Similar actions were performed in the other big cities of the West of Holland. In Rotterdam the Nazis seemed to have the largest harvest; over twenty thousand men had been picked up in one day. The previous "Razzias" had never been as severe but this meant that the Nazis were getting desperate. The newly arrived Nazis were in their element, sadistically enjoying the harsh treatment of the thousands of hungry men.

In The Hague, Kees had been at his forced labor job when the round-up came through the street where he lived. When he came home from work at ten o'clock in the morning the trucks and the soldiers were gone, doing their nasty work in another part of the city where the harvest was seemingly smaller than earlier that day. When Kees entered his house Cornelius came running towards him and told him about the excitement which had stirred up the peace in the street "Papa," he said frantically, "they took the old man from next door too!"

Johanna, who had heard her son talking to her husband also came to tell him about the great round-up which had taken place just an hour before. "It is getting really bad, Kees," she said. "The Nazis are not selective anymore. They take any man from 14 years and up, even old people. Kees, you have to hide. There are too many people needing your help and your assistance. You are too important to be caught."

The streets of the cities were becoming desolate during the day hours, but at night, with the blackouts still in place, those who had not been caught were getting even more active than before. The Nazis were actually afraid to go on patrols at night. With so many Dutch men taken from the cities they thought the threat from the Resistance might have become minor. They were very wrong and they became very sorry to think that way. In the week after the round-ups many soldiers disappeared. After the war many of them were found, drowned in the rivers which ran through the cities, weighed down with bags of bricks or sand.

The Boxers were never caught. They had their safe hiding places prepared long before. They had used those hiding places many times and the minute they had heard the trucks and the soldiers in the streets they went underground. The soldiers used children to betray their fathers or their brothers when they entered the houses. They would give them candy and asked first in a friendly tone if they knew where their daddy was. Sometimes they were slapped in their faces if they would not tell.

The children of the Resistance had been trained in what to say and how to respond to the questioning. Cornelius was a trained little liar who had never given any hint to the Nazis' questions about his dad or about the guests who were hidden underneath the floor. When the Nazis had asked him that morning, he had simply told them that his dad had died long ago. Johanna was shocked to hear her son lie like that. After the soldiers had left she took the boy on her knee and asked him, "What made you say that daddy is dead?"

The wise little guy simply answered, "Mom, you have no idea what dad and I go through when we are stopped by the Moffen every day. Dad said that this is not lying; this is saving lives and winning the war."

From that day on, Kees never went back to his "job" at Symowitz. Not only was a major part of the bomb trigger factory closed, but it could not function because of the lack of raw material. Most of the parts used at the factory were made of copper. The system in which the Nazis had supplied the factory was by 'requisition'. The word was a new one to the Dutch population. After the copper requisition, other items were systematically demanded from the Dutch. Usually one day before a requisition, the demand was made by a loudspeaker truck which would go through the streets where the requisition was going to be held. There were textile requisitions, bedding requisitions, furniture requisitions, radio requisitions, lead requisitions, art requisitions, and many more. Anything the Nazis could think of to rob from the citizens.

On the North side of the rivers which split the country the Nazis were digging in. The thousands of Dutch slaves were driven to move mountains of earth and build casemates of solid concrete in an attempt to withstand the giant Allied army which was on its way to defeat them. Any attempt to flee from the slave labor was punished with a bullet; the Nazis knew no mercy with the stubborn Dutchmen. The only goal was to get the front solidified no matter the cost of lives. If men were too old they were used anyway by bringing water and food to the workers. Very rarely old men were sent back to their homes, and if they were they would have to walk the one hundred miles or more on their own recognizance.

Kees realized that his travel times had been ended. In fact, during the day time he became his own prisoner and stayed mostly under the floor of the house, together with the last four of the many hundreds of Jews who had found refuge with Kees, Johanna, and their little son Cornelius.

At the end of November 1944, it was clear to Kees and Johanna that the war was not going to end very soon. They realized that they were going to enter into a long, cold and foodless winter. "We have to get the last four of the Jews out of the city, Kees," Johanna announced one evening.

"The only way we can do that is by night and one person at the time. I will go to the Brandwijk farm tomorrow night and take one person with me. I can no longer ride my bicycle and take Cornelius with me. We'll have to dress in black, with our faces made black and move very stealthily through the back alleys until we get out of town, and then we will have to avoid the roads and jump the creeks."

"Do you have any idea how long it will take you that way? Will you be able to reach the farm during the dark of the night and arrive before dawn?"

"I will make some calculations," was Kees' final answer.

The Nazis at the command central in The Hague made their calculations too. After having shipped over eighteen thousand men to the front lines they figured that only a few could have remained in the city. They did not know how many Boxers had escaped the roundup. Nor did they know that most of the men of the Resistance had been in hiding during the hugely scaled Razzia. It became a costly miscalculation.

Kees had not realized what the Nazis were up to either when he made his plan to go to the Brandwijk farm that night. Knowing that the soldiers would not go out in small groups, Kees thought, as the Nazis had before, that they would be on the streets in groups of six or more, in fear of being attacked under cover of the pitch dark nights.

The four Jewish guests who were still in hiding under the floor were fairly young people. They were all men who had been hiding on their own, and who had moved from place to place until they could no longer find a safe place. At that point they all knew where to go. It was not at the Jewish Council, but earlier on during the war they had been told of a policeman who was able to help them, in case their situation became desperate. The policeman patrolled a certain area of the city, always on foot. He would be under a viaduct at a certain time twice a day, and that was the place for a Jewish fugitive to find a final solution.

The policeman would give them an address and a time to go there. They were told to adhere to the directions punctually, or their rendezvous would not work. That was how they would find Kees and Johanna. They would go to the lady on the second story around the corner of the Deiman Straat and climb down into the back yard of the van Rijn residence. Through a network of people, often children, Kees would be notified of the new arrival who would announce himself with a password, as instructed by the policeman.

Now their host was going to go the extra mile. Again. Kees was going to bring one guest to the Brandwijk farm that night, but he'd have to take the blackouts into account. The blackouts were enforced more than ever, because the Allied planes flew over Holland every evening on their way to Germany with their destructive cargo. Kees made his plan carefully; he would take his bike and walk along side of it while he was still in the city. Through the back alleys and backyards they would cross several creeks by throwing his bicycle across first and then jumping the creek.

He estimated that it would take three hours to get out of the city that way. If they left at 8 o'clock that evening, they could mount the bicycle in the fields outside the city. He knew a path which was used by the farmers to take their cattle to the meadows where the Nazis would never patrol. They could then ride his bike for at least two hours without leaving the fields. The two of them would end up at the village of Voorburg, a small town heavily occupied by the German air defense. The German anti-aircraft cannons were well-guarded, but those guards would never stray far from their squadron. Kees and his charge would circumvent the village as far away from the outskirts which would take them another two hours. By that time it would be three o'clock in the morning. From there it would take two more hours through the meadows to reach the Brandwijk farm. Barring any surprises that night, they could make it by five a.m., just one hour before dawn.

Nothing went as planned during war time. Kees and Simon were not even one kilometer from the house when they almost fell over two dead soldiers, who apparently had been pulled into the alley from the main street. Kees felt an obligation to stop and examine the two; perhaps they were still alive. For a moment they stopped and looked at the soldiers. They must have been just eighteen years of age. They looked young and well fed. Hitler Juegend, he concluded, fanatics without any experience.

They heard noises coming from a side alley which connected to the main road. Suddenly four men in black outfits, their faces black with charcoal, appeared from around the corner. When they saw Kees and Simon, they pulled them down to the ground, and the bicycle was pushed into the hedge. One of them hissed, "What are you doing here? This is not a time for citizens to be in the alleys."

One of the other men, who had dropped a soldier's body next to Kees, looked closer at Kees and recognized him. "Hey, Kees, what are you doing here at this hour? It is going to be a memorable evening for the Nazis, and non-fighters like you should stay inside. We are all out tonight, the Boxers that is. Our plan is to put the fear of God into the Nazis by decimating their number. We expect them to quit coming out at night from now on."

Kees thought of the repercussions the Nazis would make the next day and asked the men about their thoughts on it. "We don't expect them to react that way this time. They will not be able to find any men in the city. They certainly won't find us, but you better be extra careful and definitely stay underground during the daytime. We know you can handle the nights, but the days will be off limits for any man to be on the streets."

They left as quickly as they had come, moving silently and practically invisible. *They must have no feeling,* these men, Kees thought, but this was war and it was a matter of kill or be killed during these brutal last days of the war.

The rest of thetrip Kees and Simon made was uneventful, but exhausting, that night. They had to go into hiding many times; twice they made a jump across a creek which ended in a splash. Their jump had been too short for the tired men. When they finally saw the farm looming up in the distance, sunrise was almost completed. They arrived in very wet clothes and shivered for the first hour. Mrs.Brandwijk had brewed them a hot drink they could not identify, but it made them burn from the inside until the shivers had subsided. Kees felt blessed to be with such warm and caring people. He was sorry he had not brought his son. Yet he knew he could not have taken him on such a dangerous journey.

The morning after Kees had travelled to the Brandwijk farm, the Nazis found more than a hundred dead soldiers in the city of The Hague. No one made an account of the total for all the major cities. It was the last, but most fearful attack by the group called The Boxers. It proved to have far reaching results and consequences.

The Generals issued a decree that repercussions would follow soon. Any man found on the streets was executed and left dead in the streets for three days. The Resistance contacted the BBC's Radio Oranje in England which made daily warnings about the Nazi's intentions. No man in his right mind went out on the streets during the day time. Unfortunately several NSB'ers were picked up and executed before they could prove their loyalty status to the Reich.

The German command was furious and looked for any excuse to avenge themselves. Their harvest for revenge proved to be very small, because the Dutch kept listening to the prohibited radio transmissions and were kept aware of the threat.

The frontlines became stronger by the day and while the Allied forces came gradually closer, a major battle was at hand and the Germans had a trump card which would stall the huge Allied armies considerably.

Chapter Twenty Three

RATIONS

—ꝏ—

Every week the Nazis posted the week's rations which the citizens were allowed to buy at astronomical prices at the dedicated stores that were controlled by the Nazis. All over the cities and towns there were poster pillars which used to be filled with advertisements for theatres and concerts or any public event. As soon as the Nazis had taken over they began using the poster pillars for their announcements.

At the end of November 1944 the week's ration read as follows:

Weekly allowance per person:

One half quart of milk.

One eighth pound of butter.

One tenth pound of lard.

One eighth pound of sugar.

One tenth pound of Jam.

One, one pound loaf of bread.

Anyone found in possession of more than the allowance will be arrested and the food will be confiscated.

The ration counted up to 80 calories per day. It was enough to stay alive and still too much to die.

In the north of the country, in the Province of Friesland, ships with loads of food were ready to sail to the west via the Nord Sea. They were held up by the Nazis and were forced to sail to Germany instead. They had a hidden agenda, this occupying enemy. If we cannot win by fighting we will win by starving the Dutch. They were close to the truth when the war came to an end. About ten percent of the population had died from hunger during the last winter of the war. It was fearfully called "The Hunger Winter of 1944/1945."

So Kees was on his mission for food at the Brandwijk farm. He stayed there for two days and rested. When he had left, he had told Johanna, "I will be back, but it may take a few days. One cannot be careful enough. So please do not worry, because I have God Almighty on my side. He is my shield and my rear guard!" With those words Kees and Johanna survived the entire war. They were never without food. Although it could be a small ration, it was always more than the Nazis had planned.

The farmer and Kees made a plan to bring a load of food to the city. It had to be carried out at night, but it had to be done on the paved roads because there was no way Kees could cross the creeks with such a load. They discussed their options all evening, but none of them would work without causing a possible calamity. Finally Kees made a decision, "Let's sleep on it and hopefully in the morning we will have a fresh idea." That night when Kees went to bed in the farmer's guest room, he prayed, "Lord, you know the need we have for food in the city. Give us an idea to bring the gift of food, which you have provided, to our people in the city without risking anyone's life."

When he woke up at five in the morning he still did not have a solution for the problem. It was two hours later at the breakfast table when the eighteen year old daughter Marie, came up with a foolproof plan.

"I know how we can get that food to the city," Marie began. "I have thought about it all night and I know this will work." When she had unfolded her plan they all agreed. It was indeed the one idea they had all been looking for. The rest of the day each of them prepared a detail of the plan and by six that evening they were ready to put it together.

Farmer Brandwijk had gone into his workshop and took the old goat cart they had not used since the beginning of the war, because the goats had all been stolen by the Nazis. He had also brought the bicycle, which Marie had used to ride to her high school before the war, and welded the cart to the back of the bicycle in such a way that it could trail the bicycle on its axle.

When he had constructed the contraption, he came riding out on the bicycle with its trailing goat cart. He made a test drive around the barn and came back with a big smile on his face. "This is great, solid and practical. Let's hope the Nazis will not take a liking to this and take it from us."

"The key is that a "grandma" is needed to survive this trip. She will have to look very fragile and delicate," Marie told Kees, with a naughty look it her eyes. They had all referred to grandma and Kees had taken it for granted that the grandma would show up sooner or later. The farmer had made a triple bottom in the goat cart. "Well," he said, "let's get this cart loaded in the barn so if we get a visitor we will not have to answer too many questions."

The farmer's wife had all the supplies ready for the job at hand. In the lowest level a hundred pounds of potatoes were spread evenly. A layer of straw went on top of that and then it was closed with the wooded floor, fitting exactly in between the sides of the cart. It really looked like the bottom of the cart. On the next level two sacks of flour were pressed flat, and on top of that, three whole hams and six freshly slaughtered chickens, were pressed into the sacks of flour.

The next wooden floor panel was put on top of the second layer of food, and then a mattress from a baby crib was placed on top of the two compartments which had been filled with food. It began to look like a regular wheel chair. Finally they placed a big cushion against the back board and the entire contraption was further dressed up with blankets. It was all done with old used cushions and greasy blankets and it gave the impression that it had been used for many years.

When Kees saw the completed product he remarked, "I wish I had had this vehicle a long time ago. I could have hauled a lot more food and I could have put Cornelius in it as a decoy. Now where is grandma, Marie? Is she coming soon? I hope you can leave soon or you won't make it to the city in time."

The time had gone by fast, and when Kees went inside to look at the old grandfather clock which had survived the stealing eyes of the Nazis, he exclaimed, "We are never going to make it to the city before curfew. It is almost eight and curfew starts at ten."

"I knew that you could not leave tonight, Kees," Farmer Brandwijk interrupted. "It is too risky to run into the dark hours and pass the hour of the curfew. Let's just enjoy another evening together and plan to leave early in the morning." Kees agreed reluctantly, thinking Johanna might get worried, but then he remembered the words he had spoken to her when he left home. She'll be in God's care. With a sigh of relief he went inside the house. They had a wonderful meal and a great evening of talk about the upcoming liberation.

When they went to sleep, they all repeated the words, "The Americans are coming, good night."

Kees had a dream that night. Before he fell asleep he was wondering who the grandma was. He had never seen a grandma at the farm. That's how the dream began. He dreamt that the war had long passed. He was retired and all his children were married and he had dozens of grandchildren who were running around in the back yard of the house at the Deiman Straat. Cornelius was teaching his three siblings how to grow flowers in the back yard. The whole yard was full of flowers and the grandchildren were picking the flowers, arms full of beautiful bouquets. Then he saw Johanna come out and the children covered her with flowers. She fell down and the next thing he saw was that she was placed in a coffin. The lid was closed and the flowers were put on top of the coffin. Then the coffin was placed on the very goat cart the farmer had constructed and Marie rode away with the coffin and the flowers on top and they began to fall all along the roadside.

Kees woke up in a sweat. He remained still and reflected on the dream he just had. Was it a sign? Was it just a figment of his imagination? Outside he heard a rooster crow; it was a sign of the early dawn and the sun would begin to rise soon. He waited at least one more hour before he got up. Still thinking about the dream, he had begun to analyze the aspects of the dream. In fact it was all beautiful in the dream, except at the end when his Johanna was taken away in a coffin.

In deep thought he came downstairs from the hayloft where he had slept. Breakfast was ready and when they sat down he could no longer keep his thoughts to himself. The big question which had caused the dream came to the group around the table – who is grandma?

Marie began to laugh and looked at her father when she uttered: "You!" Kees did not grasp the meaning of her answer and the reason for her uncontrollable laughter. Her father had to explain the situation.

"Marie has been planning this since yesterday, Kees. She is going to transform you into a grandma and no one will know because she is so darn good at it. You better believe it. This is your last breakfast as 'Kees.' Soon you will be 'grandma' so you better start acting like it right now."

Two hours later a strange contraption left the Brandwijk farm. Marie had to push hard on her bicycle pedals, but once the riding wheel chair was on its way it appeared to be easier than they had expected. The grandma in the back seat was slumped over and during the whole ride to The Hague she did not look up. They were stopped twice and the soldiers looked in empathy at the old slumped over lady in the riding contraption. They admired the young lady who was pulling the old lady around. At least she had family she could be with while they were stuck at a losing war in a strange country.

All the way to The Hague Kees was thinking about his dream. The only thing he determined to keep in his mind was the happy scene in the back yard full of flowers and the many grandchildren he had seen roaming around in his house. Was it a picture of his future? If so, it promised him a long life and many grandchildren. He decided to hold onto that promise, particularly in a time when it seemed that there was no future for any one.

Kees had never seen his son laugh so much lately as upon his arrival at the house in the big city of The Hague. When Marie finally descended from her bicycle at the end of a long and strenuous bike ride, she did not speak a word until she had ushered the old grandma into the front door. With Cornelius laughing so hard, Kees had to take immediate charge of the situation.

"Johanna, my lovely wife, help me get into a bed quickly. I bet the Gestapo is already on its way here, knowing the neighbors we have and them having witnessed this unusual arrival. They probably think I am an old Jewish lady and they will certainly ask for an Ausweiss. I have one here as old Mrs. Brandwijk from before she died. Marie here made me look exactly like her."

His prediction came true. Within minutes they banged on the front door where the bicycle contraption was still parked. They did not give it a second look, which was most fortunate because of the hidden contraband food stash. They were not very thorough in their examination this time, after they had demanded Marie's Ausweiss and that of the "old Missus." They left visibly disappointed. Kees relaxed after they had left. They seemed to be mellowing during the last days of the war.

They could not get their means of travel into the narrow hallway, so Kees asked Cornelius to go and open the doors of the Groenendijk warehouse. "Do it quickly so Marie can roll it inside, and close the doors as fast as you can. Hopefully it will not trigger another visit from the Nazis.

"It will soon be over! The Americans are coming!"

Chapter Twenty Four

A LETTER FROM AN UNKNOWN OBSERVER

This letter appeared in the underground press. The illegal newspaper, which was distributed from hand to hand, was becoming a dangerous possession in the hands of any Dutchman. If caught with it, they were arrested and sometimes even tortured to reveal the source of it

The dead and the martyred exhort us.

Rage and loathing trade places before the outrageous acts the Germans have added to their list at the onset of this year, 1945. The "Dutch " press prints exclusively what pleases the Krauts, but know that in Groningen, Almelo, Leiden, The Hague and elsewhere, rows of innocent people have been put to death like dogs, out of revenge for an attack on some traitor, some NSB-er.

The Nazis no longer search for the actual agent of such attacks. Arbitrariness is now their "law", terror is their authority. In some instances, the order was issued that corpses must lie in the street for a day and a night, exemplifying the subtlety of the Germanic taste.

With great compassion, we think of the survivors of the murdered and of the irreparable loss they have suffered as victims of Himmler's terror tactics. They experienced how in the paradise of National Socialism, a human life counts for nothing. And yet, such a life is the shrine enclosing the lasting value of democracy.

The explanation of all terror is the oppressor's anxiety. The war has almost run its course, and it is a lost cause for the Germans. On land, on the sea, and in the air, they maneuver desperately in their defense; but the Russian advance, the British bombardments of German cities, the safe arrival in the West of the Allied forces, landings behind the German invasion lines near Rome, and an invasion in the west of Europe are inevitable.

The Fuehrer himself posed the alternatives: "Sieg oder Untergang" (Victory or defeat). The chance of a victory is now gone. Defeat is the only thing left. Soon increasing bombardments will pulverize German cities. In the near future many more thousands of German men will die in vain, east, west, and south. Meanwhile Himmler's terror will rave on, furiously and more devastating than ever. And we Dutchmen can count on more hostages, more murders, more plunder and more pressure.

As soon as you feel discouraged, think of those who fell! Think of the still places, some yet unknown to us, that later will be as so many places of pilgrimage; they are the places where Dutchmen stood bravely for the last time, facing the firing squad. Think of the countrymen who suffered martyrdom in a concentration camp while you were comfortably resting at home. Think of the ones who lost everything, the destitute, the deported, those dragged away, the tortured, the mistreated and the dead. Their ranks are still growing. Every day, names are added to those of the concentration camps and prisons here in this country or abroad in thousands of Hitler's places of terror.

All these names, all these dead scream out to us and they signify for us only one thing: the freedom we have lost but which we shall regain, no matter what the cost will be.

The Americans are coming soon!

The long and cold winter never seemed to end for people who were oppressed and hungry. In the streets only women dared to go outside to search for food. The few shops that were still open could only sell to customers with distribution stamps while a soldier was watching. People would be accosted by beggars outside the stores. Sometimes fights ensued and the soldiers had to intervene.

When people talked in the streets they talked only about the upcoming liberation. But it was too cold to stand around and too dangerous to carry a bag with food. There was only safety in groups of neighbors. The men who were still in the city could not go outside for two reasons: they could either be picked up and sent to the trenches, or they could be shot on sight as a repercussion for the previous nights' activities stirred up by the Boxers.

There was a new trade on the streets in the form of food which was not hindered by distribution stamps. Tulip bulbs had proven to have a high nutritional value when grated and baked into cookies. The bulb growers who did not have a better market for their products went to the cities with boxes and bags full of tulips bulbs. Before the big roundup of men to work in the trenches, male bulb growers would bring their merchandise to the cities and sold the bulbs in the streets. Now only their wives would come and trade their wares. They would always come in groups of three for fear of being robbed by someone, or by being taken under some false pretense and robbed of their money by either NSB-ers or by the Nazis.

Johanna was in the street when a group of bulb grower's wives had arrived. They sold their bulbs for fifty cents apiece. People were flocking towards the group to buy. Money was not that scarce because there was nothing else it could be spent on. Johanna spent a hundred guilders and went home with 200 bulbs. Cornelius helped her carry the big sack of precious food.

All of a sudden the group of women was surprised by a number of Nazi trucks which came roaring around the corner into the street. Dozens of soldiers with guns ready to shoot, jumped from the trucks and surrounded the women. A sergeant yelled, "Setsen diech sofort." Some women tried to run, but they were forcefully pushed down to the ground.

Another command sounded and the soldiers each went to the women in the group, take the bag of tulip bulbs from them and at the same time demanded them to pull out their pockets and open their handbags. The soldiers took all their money and left as quickly as they had come. Some women were crying, others were cursing. The three bulb farmer's wives had been taken on the trucks with the soldiers.

Cornelius took Johanna's hand and said, "Mom, why would the soldiers do that? We did not do anything wrong. But don't worry. I still have more potatoes in the back yard. I put them under the ground together with some straw and I never told you about them. I don't like tulip bulb cookies anyway."

Through her tears Johanna could not keep herself from laughing, "You clever little boy. Because you don't like the bulb cookies, you stashed away potatoes?"

"I knew that some day we would need them Mom".

"Remember one thing, Cornelius, the Lord shall always provide no matter how difficult it may seem."

"But, Mom, I am the one who provides this time," Cornelius answered.

Johanna just shook her head and said, "One day you will understand. Come. Let's go home and dig up some of your stash."

When the two of them arrived home, Kees was waiting for them, but when he saw their happy faces he did not understand why they looked so content. He had watched the scene from behind a slit in the curtains and did not think there was any reason to be happy. Johanna told him what had occurred and about Cornelius' reaction. "Son, even if you were smart to put away some potatoes, it was the Lord who gave you the idea to do that. That is how He takes care of us in this time of need." Kees explained.

Chapter Twenty Five

AN UNEXPECTED VISITOR

The doorbell rang at ten o'clock in the evening. It was an unusual time for anyone to ring the doorbell but at least it was not accompanied by any banging on the door or by loud German voices. Kees disappeared quickly into the hall closet and behind the sliding wall. Just to be safe he went down the ladder into the underground of the house where so many Jews had been hidden during the past few years.

Johanna waited until she knew that Kees was safely in hiding to go to the door. Before she opened the door she had looked through a slit in the heavy velvet curtains to see if there was any imminent danger to be expected. The man who rang the doorbell had pressed himself against the door so Johanna could not recognize him, which made her just a little anxious to open the door. Even if it was just one person it could be a Gestapo man who had some colleagues down the street.

When she went to open the door she asked though the door "Who is it?" She did not get an answer, just the words. Quickly Johanna opened up. The voice sounded vaguely familiar, so she made the decision to trust the caller and opened the door. The man pushed himself quickly inside and pulled back the hood he had kept over his head. In surprise and to her great delight she recognized the man as she uttered, "Rabbi Lev... I mean ... I don't know what to call you anymore, but quickly let me usher you down stairs. The NSB-ers never sleep."

"Actually," Levi began: "I can play the act of Dominee De Groot if someone from the Gestapo comes. Who else could you have to tell them would come at this late hour? Besides, I should not be on the streets anyway, because they have been picking up every man they can catch. As 'Dominee' they seem to have some respect for me because I have been stopped about ten times today and they have always let me go. The Lord is watching over me, you know", he said with a smile.

Johanna showed her visitor into the front room and said, "We still have to wait a while, just to make sure no soldiers are coming to the door to check my visitor out." At that moment they heard the truck stop, then the sound of a motorcycle and voices in German. "Yes, they did it again." Johanna said. "Okay, you sit down and relax. We have handled his scenario so many times".

The banging on the door did not stop until she opened the door. They did not give her a chance to say a word and pushed themselves past her. They quickly spread throughout the house for a thorough search. She heard one of them yell at Levi and demand his Ausweiss. Johanna wisely remained in the hallway so she would not be in anyone's way. The search was over in minutes. Cornelius had been awakened and had come out of his bedroom with a sleepy face. "Why are they coming to wake me up, Mom?" he asked. "Oh, my boy, we just welcomed a visitor, Dominee De Groot," she said with an extra loud voice so the Nazis would be able to hear her, "and he came to see if he could stay here for the night." She saw that the sergeant was listening intently.

Then he barked a command, "Raush. Gehen wir mahl, dem Verdampte NSB-ers machten wieder einem falsches Alarm ."

They were gone in minutes and peace had returned in the house. Johanna went to the so familiar 'crack board' in the hallway and stepped on it. Kees waited five minutes before he went back upstairs, wondering who had caused all the commotion.

It was a pleasant surprise to see the Rabbi in the front room. The two greeted each other with a big hug. "How are you surviving the round-ups and the barricades all over in this horrible war, Levi?" Kees was admiring the courage of this young cleric who had the ability to avoid all the nasty rules and restrictions the Nazis had implemented in the country. "I am like a chameleon, Kees, and I can adjust to any color they want to see me in. Tonight I am the Dominee who is just looking for a place to sleep. In reality I am here on a mission. I have a couple of Jews I found in the ruins of Arnhem. They desperately need to get out of there because of the expected fighting which will begin any day now. The Nazis have set up a great defense system around and in the city and they expect the Americans to hit them in full force. It will flatten the city of Arnhem completely and anyone inside will be crushed. So I need two Ausweisses. I have their pictures and names with me. Hopefully you will be able to get me set up for their sake and also make arrangements to go and get them quickly, perhaps if possible, with an ambulance."

Kees thought for a moment before he answered with a question, "Who are these people that you give them such a preferential treatment?"

"They are nothing more than a couple of lonesome Jews who have been able to avoid arrest during all the years of Razzias. To me they are heroes because they have survived so far. And of course, they are God's chosen people."

Kees nodded in agreement and asked, "Let me see their pictures."

"For that I need to take some clothes off. Is there a place I can do that in private?" Levi looked at Kees apologetically.

"Of course," Kees answered, "Let me show you the bathroom here and you go ahead and take your time. Meanwhile, I'll ask Johanna to make us some self-made herbal tea she has created with the help of some chamomile and other plants my little son has grown in our backyard."

When Levi came back, Johanna had come into the room with the hot tea concoction which smelled great. "Are you sure this is not poisonous?" Levi asked with a smile. "We would not want to miss the Liberation would we?" They all laughed. It eased the tension of the entire day's events.

"If you want me to get two Ausweisses for these people, I will have to arrange it tonight," Kees said, changing the subject. "You know men can't be on the streets during the day time anymore or they will run the risk of either being shot without any justification, getting arrested and tortured for information on the Boxers, or immediately shipped to dig trenches at the frontlines. So everything I do now has to be done by night and very stealthily." Henk handed him the two Ausweisses the couple had given him and when he looked at them his eyes lit up and he was almost stuttering when he exclaimed, "Johanna, look at this! Your long lost brother and sister. We thought they had died long ago in one of the concentration camps in Nazi Germany. They are alive! It's them, look Johanna!"

Johanna grabbed the papers out of his hand and looked at the two pictures intensely. Then she began to dance and jump; she could hardly contain herself and wanted to shout. Instead she whispered, "They are alive! Thank God they are alive. Henk, where did you find them? These are my brother and sister I have not seen in more than ten years. Even long before the war they left and never let us know where they went. My goodness! God's goodness! We must bring them here a quickly as possible. They will be safe here for the rest of the war."

The rest of the evening, after Kees had left to go to the printer in the ruins of the school, Henk and Johanna talked about her long lost siblings. She shared how they had wanted to be on their own and independent from as young as when they were toddlers. She explained how they had left with their saved up money and their inheritance to seek their own prosperity and how they had chosen to remain together as partners. Finally Henk was able to tell her how and where he had found them and in what condition they had endured the war. "They are living like kings in the midst of the ruins where they have found a luxurious sanctuary. They even have a lake in front of their 'house'," Henk told her and explained the entire situation. "It sounds like a joke, but it is true. It is almost a shame to remove them from Arnhem, and from their incredible quarters, but with the invasion which is coming and with the frontlines right at the city of Arnhem, I fear for their lives. Both the Allies and the Nazis are going to throw bombs on that city and nothing can stop them. The chance they would survive is zero if they stay where they are."

It took Kees two hours to get back to the house. He had a special way to come and go without being seen. He went through the backyard of the warehouse next door and climbed up to the second floor balcony of the apartment where an old lady used to live. One day about a year ago she had gone out shopping and fell. Her head hit the curb. Another neighbor had found her and taken her to Kees and Johanna. They had called their doctor, the old home practitioner, Dr. Kalis. When he arrived she had died minutes later. The undertaker had taken her to the cemetery and buried her without any one present, except Kees and Johanna. They had conducted a small ceremony and buried her.

Kees had kept the apartment, which she apparently owned outright, and was using it as his 'office' and as the best way to come and go from his house. The staircase which went up to the apartment was always dark and there were no other neighbors who lived at the portico.

He came through the back door and shocked the two who were still talking about the discovery of Johanna's brother and sister. He handed Henk the two Ausweisses. "Wow." Henk could not keep his great admiration for the Resistance to himself. "Wow. What a great job, and so quickly. Your printer is a master forger. He should receive a medal of honor for his work when all this is over."

"We are all just doing what we can, and we are thankful to God to be alive; we don't need any medals. We give all the glory to God."

"Amen to that brother," was all Henk could say to that.

"We can sleep only a few hours because we will have to get you to the airport at the edge of the city before it gets light. There is no other way to contact the ambulance people and we don't have any paperwork to make the transport.

I hope the guys at the airport have something to make it work, but if they don't, we will have to improvise something or go to the hospital and arrange for paperwork. We have never done a transport without the proper documents and we will not take the risk, even as close to the liberation as we are."

Only three hours later two men were leaving the portico through the apartment and slipped into the dark early morning on their way to Ypenburg. Through back alleys they went, along creeks, through orchards in which the branches of the trees were leafless but whose buds were full of life, as if they held greater expectation for the coming spring than their owners had. When they came to the bridge which crossed the river *Vliet* they went under cover of the shade of the bridge and pulled the thin rope which made the small rowboat move towards them. When they had crossed the river, they crossed a small creek on a one man raft. Just a hundred meters further.

Two knocks on the almost invisible steel door of the hangar and they were where they needed to be. The man who had opened the door spoke with a soft voice, "Kees, for goodness sake, what a strange hour you've picked for a visit. What can we do for you today?" Without answering, Kees introduced Henk as Dominee De Groot before he stated his reason for coming. His first words were, "We need transportation to Arnhem, fast."

The man answered, "Of course. That is your usual reason to come here, but what makes is so urgent that you have to come so early and even before the crack of dawn? You do realize that you won't be able to go back home in half an hour, I hope?"

Kees nodded and said, "I was kind of hoping you would take me home on your way to Arnhem."

The three men sat down in the secret conference room they had created behind the fake wall of the hangar. The Resistance members went on a planning discussion. The first order of business was the necessary paperwork.

"We won't go until we have everything in hand for a trip. We could jeopardize our entire operation if we would get stopped without the proper papers. So, what do we have to transport and where to?" Jaap, the night watch of the Resistance at the hangar asked.

Henk laid the facts on the table, "We have a man and a woman in the ruins in Arnhem who need to get out of there quickly because of the impending fights which could begin at the city any day now."

"We just got them new Ausweisses without a red J on them," interjected Kees. "In addition, Henk here has to go down to Arnhem in order to get the people picked up. They are temporarily staying at a farm near the city and the farmer is not Jew-friendly."

"Let's sum up what we need," said Jaap, who took the lead in the discussion. "We have one man going to Arnhem and three people coming back to The Hague. So, all we need is one paper for the person who goes down, and will he be the same one going back? If so, we can handle that without a problem. I have a number of documents for a one man transport, both for going to Germany and for coming from Germany. We can hide the two passengers from there underneath the gurney as we have done so many times before. No papers needed for them. The only problem is how can we load them up without raising suspicion?"

Henk had a quick answer for that problem, "That, my friend, is also an easy one to solve. The farmer there is a supplier to the Nazis; they often stop by to purchase dairy products. The ambulance driver will pretend to do that. It is totally normal to see German vehicles stopping at the farm. Once the ambulance is there it can drive into the barn to load up the people anyway."

"Finally, Kees, we can drop you off at your house, provided you can get out around the corner at the café, but you will have to dress as a German soldier. Gentlemen, let's do it, and do it now, and as fast as we can. I'll wake up a driver. Kees, put on these." He handed Kees a German soldier uniform, complete with boots.

Six minutes later, the door of the big airplane hangar opened and an ambulance raced towards the exit of the airport. Close to the gate the driver turned on his siren. The sentry on guard duly opened the barrier.

Chapter Twenty Six

EXODUS FROM THE LYON'S DEN

—⁂—

The frontlines, which had literally been built by the Dutch slave laborers who had been picked up by the Nazis in the big cities, were built in rows of one kilometer behind each other. Three rows of trenches had been dug and concrete bunkers had been built to house the cannons, the machine guns, the command posts and the supply depots. It seemed to be a masterpiece of German engineering.

The farms scattered between the trenches had been warned to evacuate at a moment's notice. What the German planners did not know was that at several of those farms numbers of Jews were in hiding. The Resistance was notified of the problem by several farmers who had come to The Hague with the problem. The message ended up with Kees who made a plan to gather a group of Resistance leaders to discuss the problem further and find a plausible solution.

Late in the month of February 1945, a meeting was scheduled at the Groenendijk warehouse. It was a pitch dark night and freezing cold when the men began to arrive. They came in baker box-bicycles, three at a time. The riders were women who acted as salespersons, and miraculously not one of them had been stopped by a Nazi patrol. That evening even the neighboring NSB-ers did not cause a Gestapo visit. For two reasons the activities of the NSB-ers were tapering off. For one, a lot of them had fled to other towns where they would not be known to anyone as they came as innocent fugitives. Often times they would concoct heart wrenching stories to be accepted. The other reason was that they were laying low and trying to become friends with their neighbors, faking that they had never been NSB-ers. After the war lists were compiled of names of known NSB-ers and a country wide search resulted in many arrests and convictions.

When the eighteen members of the Resistance leadership had all arrived at the Groenendijk warehouse, Kees had them come through the backyard and climb upstairs to the old deceased lady's apartment. From there they could leave one by one after they had come down the staircase into the dark portico. They would easily slip into the cover of a pitch dark, icy cold night.

The meeting began when Kees told the men, who were anxious to help in any situation, that at about twelve farms in the region of the frontlines at least 185 Jews were in grave danger of being caught and deported at the very end of the war. At the very least, they were at risk of being killed in the ensuing cross fire by either the Allies or the Nazis.

What are our options? We need to take action as soon as possible. How can we move 185 people right from under the noses of the Nazis? Where do we relocate them? For how long will they have to stay at a new location? Do we put them all together or separate them? How do we feed them? The questions kept coming, and Kees and one of his closest friends were taking notes.

After at least half an hour they had a great number of questions down on paper, but no answers. Frans Knecht, Kees's closest friend and colleague, stood up and made an announcement, "I am going to write all these questions on the wallpaper here. I'll write it in big letters so that everyone can read it. Let's try to do it in order of importance or rather, urgency. What would be our first problem, gentlemen? Do you have any suggestions?"

One of the men took the initiative to say what he thought. "I think our first priority is where are we going to put them and how, in one big location or in many different ones? A school or church would be feasible but where is one out of the way of the frontlines and in a place where there is little or no Nazis patrol?"

Kees answered his question with a question for the crowd. "Does anyone have an answer to that? Schools are not open so that could be a possibility, but how are we going to explain the activity, of people coming and going, to take care of them to deliver food and whatever is needed? What about a church?"

One of the men raised his hand. "I know a church right smack in the middle of the town of Rijswijk, which is only used for Christmas and Easter. The Nazis never patrol around there because it is at the end of a long driveway. I am one of the caretakers of the church and I know how we could use it.

"I would need to know how long we would need it, but it does have a basement that we could use as a hiding place in case someone betrays it. Also, we have a cleaning company which arrives there every day with a box bicycle full of cleaning material. I was thinking we could use that to bring in food." Many heads were nodding at these suggestions.

"It could work," another man interrupted, "but I would like to see it first and study the movements of the Nazi patrols around that church."

Kees posed the second question which had been put in order of importance, "Gentlemen, let's address the removing of a hundred and eighty five people from the frontlines, where it is crowded with German soldiers. A lot of the Jewish fugitives are older and would not be able to walk for a long ways. Could we move them at night or during the daytime?" No one made a suggestion. Every head was bowed down and in deep thought about a possible solution. It remained very quiet for a long time until finally, Frans raised his hand.

"Something in my mind is stirring about a solution. I am not quite clear exactly but I am willing to put it on the table and see if we could go that route." Many eyes were looking expectantly at Frans, who had a reputation for unique solutions and ideas. "Before I tell you more, I have a question. Does anyone know how our men are getting fed while building those wretched trenches?"

A person who had been silent for a long time stood up and gave his story: "My dad was picked up two weeks ago. He worked at the frontlines for three days when he collapsed. He is seventy eight years of age and it blew my mind why they had taken him in the first place.

"He told me that, every morning they get boiled oatmeal, cooked in water, probably right from the river because it tasted horrible, and they have to work on that all day. In the evening they give them a watery soup with some meat in it. My dad questioned the origin of the meat and thought it might be from dogs and cats. That too tasted horrible. All the workers were very hungry, but if they complained, they would get nothing at all."

"I think my plan might work." Frans Knecht, who had stood up again began to explain what he had in mind. "We should organize a food drive for the workers in the trenches. The food drive could be organized by that particular church congregation in Rijswijk. Of course it can only be done by women, but we can mix in with them, and dress up like them. We can even make a public campaign out of it and it will please the Nazis if we take care of our men and make them stronger to work for them. For the transport we can get the farmers' wives to come with their horses and wagons, you know those big ones on which they haul straw and heavy stuff. On the way to the trenches we will have twenty people on each wagon and on the way back we'll have thirty, all women, or looking like them." It was totally silent in the room when Frans finished. One of the men began to applaud, but he quickly realized he could not make any unnecessary sounds.

Kees did agree that this was one of Frans' most brilliant plans and gestured for the attention of all those present. "Gentlemen we need to split up in groups of four and work out the details of this idea. Let's do it right now and finish this plan in the next hour. And please, do it quietly, we don't need any unwanted visitors."

The next two days had been very hectic for the group of Resistance men. On the third day the legal, (Nazi approved) newspaper published an article which could have been German propaganda. It began with the title:

Our hardworking men are hungry

The Hervormde Kerk in Rijswijk is going to gather food for our men in the trenches. The German leadership has approved the drive and is allowing the women to take the food to the thousands of men who are working for the German army at the frontlines. The German command welcomed the effort of the church women and apologized that they did not have sufficient food supplies for the workers. Any person who has a husband, a son or a father working at the trenches is asked to help by bringing some food and also volunteers are asked to go with them to hand out food. It will be a three day event and the German troops will assist with entrance and exits to the frontlines and to the tents where the men are sleeping. Come ladies, our men need us.

Several Resistance men had left the city in the very early morning hours after the meeting. Under cover of a dark night they each had an assignment to visit one of the farms within the frontline area and prepare the Jews in hiding for the plan.

It took them two nights to get to their destination. During the day time they went in hiding in haylofts or shacks, in orchards or stables; only to become active again after the sun was well gone behind the horizon. Each one of them had an assignment to brief the farmers and their people in hiding. They had to prepare them for the days to come and to change the men into women with any clothes they could muster up at the farm or at one of their neighbors.

Frans and Kees were the overseers of the plan. They remained in the city to organize all the activities. They stationed themselves at the church and dressed like women. To their great surprise many people came to bring food and too many had come to volunteer. Other men had been assigned to go to the farms surrounding the city and ask for help with their horses and wagons. They could be driven by the farmer's wives who welcomed the plan with great enthusiasm.

Time and again the Resistance members answered the same questions, are the Nazis really supporting this? The answer was always, as long as it is an all-women effort.

It was a comical sight to behold when the first wagon train left the Hervomde Kerk in Rijswijk, that third day after the plan was born. It was a beautiful, cold sunny winter day in March of 1945. Eight wagons, drawn by skinny underfed horses, were filled with women sitting on boxes of food. In front of the wagon train was a German patrol car and behind it as well. People, who saw the wagon train coming by, shook their heads. *The Nazis have tricked them again,* poor women, they thought.

The plan was to get at the frontlines in six hours, feed the men at all the different places they were working and return to the city at night. The lady drivers had been instructed which roads to take once they had unloaded their food.

The Resistance men who had prepared the Jews for their departure would be ready in the tall grass along the side of the road. Eight or ten Jews were to get on each wagon and sit in the center surrounded by the women from the city.

At 11 o'clock, that same night, the first seventy eight Jewish fugitives arrived at the Hervormde Kerk in Rijswijk. The first day of the exodus from the frontlines was a day to remember and celebrate. This time they had defeated the Nazis by moving seventy eight valuable lives from right out of the lion's den.

For two days the system worked equally perfect. Even at the church no Nazis ever came to see what was going on. Operation exodus was completed without incidents. Two weeks later some of the men who had been rounded up for their slave labor at the frontlines came home. They were hungry and tired but no one ever found out what had been happening behind the scenes.

Kees came home exhausted from three days of directing and organizing keeping secrecy at the same time. The food supply was completely exhausted as well and he decided to go on a food gathering search the following night. He afforded himself a day and a night of rest, but then he had to go and find some food. The Nazis had finally relented from rounding up men and there were rumors that the rest of the men from the frontlines would also be send home soon.

Chapter Twenty Seven

FAMILY REUNION

Johanna came to the front room and asked Kees when he expected the ambulance from Arnhem to come back. "They should have been back here yesterday; I hope they did not run into a nasty bunch of Krauts who could be thinking that they had found the catch of their life time." At that very moment they heard the horn of an automobile in front of their house. Johanna ran to the curtains and peeked out. Excitedly she screamed, "They're here!" Kees quickly open up the Groenendijk warehouse. He was already on his way – the only way he could go to open the warehouse was through the back yard.

Since the last Jews in hiding had left, Kees had closed off the access through the lower level of the house. The doors opened a few seconds later and the ambulance drove inside; a minute later with the doors closed, four people came from the vehicle and stretched themselves after the ten hour trip. Lucas and Ruth Schmall had to adjust their eyes to see who the people were they were going to stay with, until the end of the war would arrive.

Henk had not told the two that they would be re-united with their very own sister. It took a few minutes for them to see clearly and then Ruth recognized her sister. Tears welled up in her eyes when she embraced her long forgotten sister. Johanna uttered, choking away her emotions, "I really thought you were long dead. How did you manage to stay alive? You'll have to tell me all about it, but first I need to hug my long lost brother and then we'll have some soup."

Johanna, always resolute, showed the way to their house through the back yard. She had made a big pot of vegetable soup with lard in it which gave it a really good taste. She introduced her brother and sister to Cornelius who had never met his aunt and uncle. He could not wait to tell the two about his little back yard farm. Then he said, "Mom if I had known that your family was coming I would have slaughtered a duck and you could have put that in the soup too." Johanna told them about her dexterous son, how he was always thinking about growing or raising something which could be used for food. "Too bad it is winter. You should have seen our backyard last summer and in the fall. It sure helped us to survive this horrible hunger winter."

Chapter Twenty Eight

INUNDATION AS DEFENSE

Kees had to get the ambulance out of the warehouse and exchanged a few words with the driver. "Did you have any problems on the way back? I was just wondering what had taken you so long."

But the driver shook his head, "No, we were not stopped even once, but what kept us was the inundation. You did not hear about what is happening in the entire south of the country?"

Kees shook his head. "No, I don't know what you are talking about. What inundation?"

The Americans, the Allies I should say, are coming and at one place they have already crossed the river, The Rijn. Immediately after they had crossed, the Nazis flooded the Betuwe. There is water everywhere and it stopped the approaching Allies right in their tracks. Every time the Allies break through, the Nazis flood the area."

When Kees took in the news of the inundation, he realized what they had accomplished in the past week was an act of God. If the Jews, which they had taken out of the farms at the frontlines would have been caught by the inundation they would have all drowned. He could not wait to visit Frans and tell him this breaking news. He now knew why it all had gone so smoothly and without a hitch. It was a Godly plan, and he was used to organize and perform it. He felt proud and humbled at the same time.

He thanked the ambulance driver abundantly. He felt extra grateful this time and asked him how he had made it through the watery flooding. "It was just a matter of taking more and more turns and in some cases a complete turn-around to find an un-flooded road. The traffic, especially the Nazi traffic, was very heavy and it seemed to all be going in the direction of Germany."

"Well thank you my friend, I hope to see you soon in the liberation parades."

The garage doors closed quickly behind the departing ambulance. Perhaps we are becoming too conscious in these final days. He decided to keep it that way until the Allies marched through the streets of The Hague.

It could not be much longer, he thought, the Americans are coming!

Soon, yes, very soon! Thank God.

In such a thankful mood he went into the house and greeted Johanna's brother and sister. A few minutes later he stood up and said, "I have to go to Frans with some news that he is not going to believe. I'll be back in an hour. Keep some soup for me please."

"You are not going to believe what is happening at the frontlines," Kees blurted out when he entered Frans' house. The usual procedure was done before he could enter and Frans was surprised to see Kees at this late hour. "The Nazis are flooding half of our country in order to keep the allies from advancing. Have you listened to Radio Oranje lately and have they made any mention of it? If not, we need to notify them as soon as possible. Do we still have access to the transmitter in the school basement where the printer is located?"

"We do and let's go," Frans answered resolutely.

It took only ten minutes of carefully moving through the dark back alleys to get to the ruins of the school. It was a quiet night. The soldiers seemed to be too scared to go on patrol in the streets. When they reached the cellar they greeted the printer who was always working on some illegal document. Kees had never seen him not work. Finally the three could talk freely. No sound could travel outside through the enormous mountain of rubble.

"Where on earth did you get this information, Kees, and how long has this been going on?"

"We were just there two days ago and nothing was flooded. What a miracle that we rescued all those Jews out of that region. What is happening to the farmers whose farms are under water and what is happening to all the Dutch slave laborers?" Frans was known to fire off dozens of question before he expected an answer, so Kees told him to take a deep breath.

"I had sent an ambulance to pick up a couple of people in Arnhem on a request from Rabbi Levi. He had found two Jews who had lived through the war all this time and who he felt needed to get out of there because of the coming Allied offensive. Do you remember making the two Ausweisses I requested for them?" Kees asked, now addressing the printer who nodded his head in silence. "Well, they turned out to be Johanna's long lost brother and sister.

"Anyway, the ambulance driver took two days longer than we expected to return. When I asked him what happened he told me of the inundation. He had to find ways to get back here and the water was everywhere; even the Nazis were trying to get through. Most of them were going in the direction of Germany."

"Hallelujah," Frans exclaimed. "So the Nazis think they can win the war by flooding the country? Don't they know that the Allies have boats and parachute troops? Are they going out of their minds by drowning all those people on the farms, and drowning their livestock as well?"

"We need to send a message to the government in England right now! That's why we came here at this hour." The secret and illegal radio transmitter was in a different room far from the printing room. They had placed it there to avoid the Nazis finding it, and also to prevent them from stumbling into the print shop.

Anytime the transmitter was used the Germans would zoom in on it and try to decipher the messages. They had intercepted many messages but they had never been able to locate the sender. This time the Germans did not even listen to the transmission. Their minds were occupied with how they would be able to get back home and avoid being captured by the advancing Allied troops.

The message they sent was short and to the point: *Germans are purposely inundating all the land north of the great rivers and in Zeeland. Many farmers and their livestock drowned. Res # lll.*

The two friends left the building quickly. They did not know that the Nazis were not listening at this time, but they would never take a risk of being detected. They did not speak a word on the way to Frans' home. Any sound could betray them even though the NSB-ers had lost their interest in betraying people. They, too, were worried about how to get out without repercussions. Once inside the house Kees told Frans that he needed to go and find food the next day. "Do you have any suggestions where I could go? Most of the farms are out of everything, even sugar beets."

"Go to the Wieringermeer. You might find something there," was all Frans could suggest.

Even though every citizen was beyond hungry and people were dying in the streets, there was still an atmosphere of optimism, an expectation that the end was in sight. The soldiers seemed to become mellow and even friendly. The generals were allowing things which had never happened before.

Chapter Twenty Nine

A TEMPORARY SOLUTION TO HUNGER

—⸙—

In a country north of Holland, in the Kingdom of Sweden, there had not been a war. The Swedes decided not to participate by declaring neutrality. They were aware of the hunger situation in Holland and had asked the General Commander of the Nazis in Holland to be allowed to bring in humanitarian help. For weeks a dozen or so fishing boats had been ready to sail across the Nord Sea into the harbors in the west of Holland. The Swedish humanitarian leaders had been negotiating with the generals for a safe passage and guidance from a couple of patrol boats. Finally at the beginning of March, they had reached an agreement. Within days the fleet of fishing boats arrived at the Dutch harbors along the seaside.

The Resistance had received a message from England to arrange for distribution, but they feared that the Nazis would at last be able to arrest them. Kees and Frans had arranged another meeting to find a way to create an orderly distribution. "We need to get the help of the German soldiers, but how are we going to play that?" Kees asked the group of Resistance men.

"Let's do what we just did with the evacuation of the Jews from the frontlines." Frans thought aloud. "We can have two women visit the command center and ask for help. At least they should appreciate the help and, after all, they gave their permission for the Swedes to come."

Once again Frans' idea was adopted and Johanna and Bertha were assigned to go to the command center. It turned out to be a feast for the entire population of the Western cities. White bread! They had not tasted it for two years, and instead of lard and cheese, real butter, like only the Swedes can make.

The citizens swarmed towards the harbors to pick up their allotment. There was a sense of liberation already; but it lasted only two days and when the bread and butter and cheese was all eaten, the hunger seemed even more severe. They still had to survive for more than six weeks until the real liberation had been achieved. But no one knew that beforehand. For all they knew it could be six months, or more. All they said everyday:

The Americans are coming!

Kees had postponed his trip to search for food because of the arrival of the Swedes. After three days Johanna told him, "If you don't go and get something to eat for us we will be like the people who are roaming the streets scavenging for food."

"Is it that bad?" Kees asked. He had not realized that the scarcity of food was rapidly getting worse in the cities. There were no stores open nor were there any stores that had anything to sell. The inundation in the south had disabled any transport to come through, and in that part of the country where food was usually produced, the little provisions which had been preserved were rotting away beneath the waters of the inundation.

It was on a crisp, early spring morning that Kees said to Cornelius, "It's time to go on a scavenger hunt to the Wieringerwaard. We have not been there for a while, but I still know some farmers there. Let's hope they have something to sell to us." To their surprise there were no road blocks or barricades anymore. The streets and roads were full of people who roamed the country side in search for something to eat. Kees was prepared to haul a good size load back to the city; He had the side bags on his bicycle, the box underneath Cornelius' seat, and a small suit case was tied behind the boy's back. To merely ride the bicycle was difficult because of all the people who were on the streets.

The chaos was indescribable. Some people had lost their minds and were screaming in the streets, "Hunger, Hunger," before they dropped down on their knees and cried their hearts out. Kees was wondering if he should go back home or continue in the turmoil. He did not like to expose his son to such unrest and hopelessness. But then his own stomach told him to go on or soon he might become one of them.

On the way, tulip bulb vendors were offering their wares to the passersby. But everyone was looking for something better, food which was more nutritious and satisfying. The sick smell of bulb cookies make the stomach turn. Some people were so horrified of the taste of tulip bulb cookies, that they would rather drop dead than eat them.

Passing through the masses of fugitives was the occasional convoy of trucks, loaded with Nazis and the loot they had robbed from stores or private homes.

They honked their way through the cursing masses. Some of people raised their fists against the passing soldiers who had only one goal at this time – how to get out of the country and back to their families alive. Radio Oranje was openly broadcasting three times a day. They were making announcements which made the soldiers even more anxious to keep going. The NSB-ers were following their masters, in secret, for fear they would be stoned by the citizens.

The news came through that the Americans had crossed the River Rijn and that they were filling the holes in the dykes to stop the inundation. Broadcasts from Radio Oranje warned the people to stay calm and hold off on any celebrations. *We are not free yet, and do not provoke the Nazis because they may still shoot and kill the citizens.*

City after city was captured and liberated by the Allies, but in the big cities of the West war raged on, continuing scarcity of every daily need, living in dirt and disorder.

The only rumor which had been verified was that the Nazis in the west of the country were going to stay and fight. The old Bismarckjuegend, those third rated troops, had gone. Those who had remained behind were the fanatics, the ones who would rather die than surrender. But where was the population going to stay when the fighting for the cities would begin? The basements were filled with water and most public buildings were in ruins. People were sick of the tulip bulb cookies, but it was the last of the possible edible nourishment and it did fill the stomach.

A new problem was looming over the western cities. The water supply was virtually nonexistent. The water plants were closed and the taps didn't surrender any more water. People were warned to stock up on water if they could still find some. Others were filling their galvanized buckets in the rivers and boiling the water on bonfires. The war was anything but over, and the twilight zone in which everyone seemed to live was extended day by day. Each family was on its own. The Resistance couldn't do much anymore. Everyone was just waiting until the day would come when the great news would be announced: WE ARE FREE!

The Americans were preparing to drop food boxes in the beleaguered and hungry cities. A number of messages were broadcast on Radio Oranje about the drops. Let it be done orderly. Avoid chaos. Put a man at each drop site. No one was ready; everyone was too hungry to have it distributed in an orderly fashion. Kees and Frans were having a meeting again, this time about the Royal advice. "They have no idea what is going on in the streets, those leaders in England. They should come here and take a look at all those hungry people, roaming the streets.

"They will run to the drop sites and grab whatever they can, and the Nazis will even participate in the run on food." It was Kees who had brought up the problem, and he announced that he was open to suggestions. "But before you have any idea how to solve this, I need to tell you that the drops will be during the day time and it will happen every day at a set time. What time, I don't know yet. I would like to suggest a special drop site where the people cannot come and then we can distribute it properly."

They were interrupted by the sound of low flying planes, big American freight planes. When they ran to the back yard they saw crates coming out of the planes. "Are they insane?" Frans asked incredulous, "They are dropping right over the city." Without warning they were going to drop. The crates were falling on the houses and in the streets. Luckily there was no traffic in the streets, but what was going to happen once the crates had landed one could only imagine.

"We need to go out there and prevent this predicted chaos. They were talking about it on Radio Oranje. Come, Frans. Let's go and do something," Kees yelled above the roaring noise of the planes. When they came to the street in front of the house, they found what they had feared was already in progress. It seemed like everyone was outside and where two crates had dropped, a mountain of people were climbing over each other to grab anything that had come out of the crates that had burst open on impact, and dispersed its contents in a large circle. With arms full, people fought their way out of the crowd. No one knew what they had grabbed. Among the citizens were German soldiers too. They did not have their guns this time, their hunger and greed had driven them like animals to their prey.

Dropping food in the field.

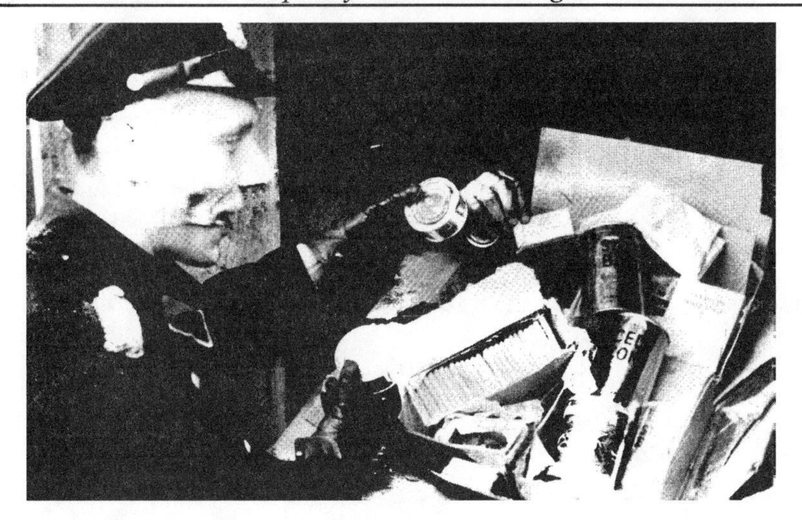

The contents of the food boxes:
Spam, biscuits, diced bacon, beans, sardines,
chewing gum, cigarettes and chocolates

Kees and Frans just stood there and shook their heads. "We will have to take control of this, but first we need to notify the leadership in England of what is going on here. They must understand that this will cause deaths and more trouble than they can foresee. We must tell them that the drops cannot continue this way. I think they should drop food like they did with the arms and ammunition just a few weeks ago. Perhaps even at night, when no one can see what and where it is taking place. The field next to the airport is the safest place for that." Without saying it, they began to run towards the ruins where the print shop was located. "We better not be careless and give away the location of our transmitter." Simultaneously they looked back to see if they had been followed by anyone.

"Times are changing quickly now," Frans remarked. "We are going to see freedom very soon and the Krauts are feeling the end coming too." They went on in their usual careful way into the ruined school building, down to the long underground hallway and entered the door of the printer's sanctuary.

"Sorry to disturb you in your crafty job. We have to notify the government in England about the food drops. It has just begun, and pandemonium is already rampant. The planes dropped their cargo right in the streets and on top of the buildings and everyone is out there fighting for a share of it. We have to tell them to stop and to give them a dedicated drop site so the population, as well as the German soldiers ,cannot just grab what they want."

The printer went with them to the room where the transmitter was located and offered a suggestion, "I could print a quick pamphlet which can be handed out to the people that asks them to stay inside when they hear the planes coming over."

"I don't think that would do any good, because everyone is hungry. They act like animals just to get something out of the crates. The problem is with the Nazis. If they come and control the drop with their guns, we have no chance and we will have nothing to distribute to the citizens." Kees answered.

The message that went out to Radio Oranje and to the Dutch government in exile was urgent but graceful:

> *We are excited and thankful for the food drops. We heeded your warnings to take charge of the distribution. Please help us coordinate the drop site. Today's drops were done right over the city; crates fell on the streets and even on the buildings. They need to be dropped with parachutes because even from a low altitude they burst open and the citizens as well as the Nazis jump on them like animals of prey. We, the Resistance of The Hague, suggest having the drops done in fields outside the cities, at pre-planned times, so that we can take care of a proper distribution. For The Hague, we suggest to use the same site as that which was used for "equipment" previously. Even the same time could work very well. We are standing by for an answer. Res.III*

Kees and Frans sat down and waited for a reply, they could never ask for a reply before, but this time they were confident that the transmission and the re-transmission would not be traced by the Nazis, who were more concerned about their safe departure than about illegal radio activity. "I am very curious as to what were the contents of the crates that were dropped today. The first thing we need to do with the next drop is to make an inventory list in order to plan fair distribution. We also need to find places to bring the food for distribution, I was thinking of just bringing it to all the former grocery stores."

A crackling sound came out of the transmitter. For the first time in all the almost five years of war a voice came through on the receiver.

> *"Res.III, we have heard your message of ten minutes ago. We are contacting the commander of the dedicated squadron at the air force base to see what can be done. We appreciate your concern and we have taken notice of your suggestions. Please stay at your transmitting location so we can get you more specific instructions about further drops. We have a huge warehouse full of food and we are determined to get it all to you without delay. God bless you for all your effort. COM.I."*

The two Resistance men were elated to finally have had the ability to have direct communication with the commander in chief in England. "We better get all our men together as soon as possible and begin the planning for tonight. I am convinced that England will go for the night drops and we better be ready." Kees told his friend.

"There is one thing we are forgetting, or we have not thought of. How, are we going to transport all those crates? Of what I have seen, they must weigh about a hundred pounds, so we better have some really strong men at the drop site."

It was Frans with his practical mind who had spoken and Kees was listening while his mind was racing to find a solution. He realized that they needed lots of men, but they would all be Resistance men and perhaps a group of the Boxers. Could they expose themselves to the Nazis at this time? It was a question neither Kees, nor Frans, could answer intelligently at this time.

"We better set up a meeting quickly," but where! It was broad daylight, and around ten a.m. "Why don't you go, Kees, and visit the Boxers' office. See if we can have a meeting there, this afternoon. We will have three hours to notify everyone. I'll stay here and wait for the message, that way we can hit two birds with one stone." *Frans is such a practical person, what would I do without him,* Kees thought.

Chapter Thirty

THE END IS ALMOST THERE

When the need is at its peak, the solution is always near!

It was an expression that could be heard every day in the war-torn country of Holland. The hunger was becoming unbearable for everyone, including the leaders and the soldiers. It was one of the reasons why the Nazis were mellowing out, almost to the point of negligence of their duties.

Rumors made the news that the Russians and the Americans had shaken hands in Berlin. Many cities in Germany were indeed in the hands of the Allied troops, and further to the east the Russians had captured many cities of the Nazis. Just imagine if the Russians had not been met halfway in Germany. The Americans not only defeated the Nazis, they confronted and stopped the Russians in their quest to conquer Europe.

The west of Holland, the provinces of the country called Noord-and Zuid Holland, are completely isolated from the rest of the country. The remaining clique of Nazis, estimated at one hundred and fifty thousand troops, were told to defend the western part of Holland, no matter what.

The Americans were getting closer and closer. The citizens of the West were talking together in the streets, sharing rumors and news, true or not true. In the City of Zutphen in the East of the country, close to the city where the brave Tante Riek used to help fugitives out of the country, a fierce battle broke out between fifteen hundred Nazi boys and the Allieds. These boys, barely fifteen years and older, fought from the manholes and killed fifty Allied soldiers. They had to be burned out of their positions with flame throwers. Totally burned and mentally mutilated most of the boys died a cruel death, for what? The news of more and more conquered cities increased day by day.

The country was practically covered with water. Everywhere river dykes had been breached. It was practically impossible to go anywhere in the country.

Down the street was a family of eight, who had just arrived from the city of Arnhem. They were telling everyone that it took them fourteen days to finally get to The Hague. No one had room for them. A group of soldiers pointed them to a house around the corner. There are soldiers living in part of the house and the owner was willing to give the family of eight living accommodation at a price.

The soldiers promised them food for the coming days; the neighborhood raised questions about the situation. Are the new arrivals NSB-ers? Johanna, always wanting to help people, asked the owner of the house if she knew that they were NSB-ers. The lady was furious and scolded, "You are no better than they. They are human beings; that is all that matters for me." *Time will tell, if they are traitors and the lady accommodating them shall have to face the consequences, too,* Johanna thought to herself.

Finally the news came – the battle of Arnhem was over! The Allieds and the Nazis had large numbers of casualties and the city was completely demolished by the bombs and cannons from both sides. The final breakthrough caused a ripple of excitement throughout the world. Now the end was only days away. The Nazis in the west finally had become scared. Soldiers tried to desert. Many knocked on doors of the citizens and begged to take them in.

On the first day of May 1945 news spread that Hitler had died. Supposedly, he died of an illness; that was the first rumor which was spreading. Later that day, new information came through saying that he had committed suicide. Whatever way he died, the people did not care. The monster was gone, and he left behind a broken world with millions dead on every front. He had reaped what he had sown – death and destruction, genocide and misery, chaos and disorder. Even several Nazi soldiers were observed celebrating Hitler's death.

The Dutch had a different outlook, one of peace, justice and neighborly love. It was the voice of victory which will always win.

The next day, an official newscast from Radio Oranje, reported the death of Hitler and General Doenitsz, his successor, was determined to continue the war. The harbor of Rotterdam had been reopened, so ships with food could now be brought into the country. German trucks were used for the food transportation. The German soldiers acted as if that was their normal everyday duty.

The soldiers were no longer carrying guns. Only handguns were worn and they were probably not loaded. No one intended to find out if they were. The war seemed to have ended but where was the peace? Rumors reached Holland about capitulating troops, even entire brigades. They may have been rumors, but they still gave hope that the end was very near. Apparently peace had come to several European countries. Why not in Holland?

The meeting at the Boxers' "office" went well. Over a hundred men had come together and discussed the food distribution options. Leo, the militant leader of the Boxers was still thinking in terms of a battle, expecting strong resistance from the other side. Kees and Frans acted as the antithesis of Boxer thinking. "Even though it is still war, the Nazis are non-militant now, and I believe if we ask for trucks they will provide them. It may be at a price, perhaps in the form of a favor, or for some of the food. In my opinion, that is worth it, to the cause of getting food to our citizens quickly," Frans encouraged the large group of men.

The Boxers did not oppose this idea and Frans went on, "If they would give us six trucks we can also use the two that we own, the ones we used at the slaughterhouse mission. That makes eight trucks of food which we can equally divide among sixteen stores; we can plan the loading of the trucks accordingly, so that each store will get the same assortment."

"What about the fair distribution, is there a system you propose?" One of the Resistance men called out.

"I have a theory about that, too. Please bear with me," Frans answered. "We can expect at least a week of droppings. That is what the Tommies have promised, so we divide the alphabet into six equal parts: Day 1, A to D. Day 2,E to H, etcetera. The people with the first letter of their last name with these letters come and get their allotment. All we have to do is post this system at each of the distributing stores and all will be equally provided."

Most men agreed, but some had suggestions which would refine the system even further. Kees announced, "All who are in favor of this plan raise your hand." Ninety four hands went up. Kees and Frans made a quick count and then Kees asked, "All who are against this please, raise your hands " Only fifteen hands went up. "Even though, we have an overwhelming majority for the plan, we would like to talk to all those who are against it, just to be aware of any valuable objections. In case we come up with any important issues, we will discuss those in the meeting. Gentlemen, let's take a break for a half hour, so we can listen to those who had objections." Kees and Frans stood up and waved their hands to those who had voted "no". They went to one of the side room and had their discussion.

Never, during the previous five years of war, had there been a meeting this large. Some of the Boxers had become a little nervous about the gathering of so many men. One of them remarked, "We better all leave through the church after this meeting. I can ask the pastor to have a short church service with us, so in case someone sees us coming out of the church everyone will have the same answer – 'We just went to Church.'"

When the person who had voiced his opinion approached Leo about it, Leo laughed, "You are still in a militant mode, my friend. The war is practically over. Don't worry. The Gestapo has lost their sting!"

The meeting had lasted four hours and when it was all over, most men had a task to fulfill. That night the first major food drop took place. The plan had worked thus far, but no one knew that trouble was still on the horizon!

Kees, who had to perform the task of going to the airport and asking for seven trucks had been able to secure them after the airport commander had made a call to the central Nazi command in The Hague. At eleven thirty that evening a convoy of nine trucks went through the gates of the airport. No one noticed the exact number of trucks, and that proved to be a blessing later.

In each truck were two soldiers, a driver and an armed companion. When Kees had noticed the armed soldiers in the trucks, he had objected to the dispatching commander. "Why guns at this time? You know we would not need those."

The man had shrugged his shoulders and explained, "Orders from The Hague." Kees did not like it, but what could he do about it?

The convoy of trucks was lined up next to the field where just months before contraband arms had been dropped off and spirited away to the Dutch underground army. Now they were able to receive help from England with the help of the Nazis. It was hard to accept the situation, even for Kees, who had joined Frans in preparing for the arrival of the planes.

Exactly at the time they had transmitted, the planes arrived over the field near the airport Ypenburg. Six planes made their drop, rose again and returned for a second drop. The men on both sides of the drop site corridor had almost run towards the dropped packets when they noticed the planes were returning for a third time. Frans yelled to Kees, who was just twenty meters away, but the roaring noise of the planes prevented audible conversation no matter how loud one yelled. Kees gestured to Frans to come closer. When he did he still had to yell, "We would not have been able to load all this up in seven trucks. Aren't you glad we had our own two trucks as well?"

"I thought we should put one of our men in each of the Nazi trucks, to show them the way to the stores. The Nazis agreed to this and I have given nine men an address where they will go to."

"Excellent idea. When are they getting on the trucks?" Kees asked. "We have one of our own trucks blocking the exit to the road just in case they 'forget' that little detail," answered Frans.

The plan was well prepared, and the Nazi trucks duly took a Resistance man into their cockpit. The convoy began to move out of the field and onto the road towards the city.

It happened when they crossed over the Hoornbrug. Suddenly, tanks drove up to the convoy and surrounded the trucks, forcing them to stop. Hundreds of soldiers came from every direction. Kees and Frans who had followed the convoy on their bicycles saw it all happen in a few minutes. They quickly went down the side of the bridge, where they were in the protection of darkness. They dropped their bicycles in the tall grass and watched awestricken at what was happening to their faithful men and the cargo of food. They couldn't believe how the Resistance men were lead away by Gestapo officers.

When the convoy began to move, escorted by armored trucks and tanks, Kees and Frans realized that the mission had completely failed. "I wonder what will happen to our own two trucks. I hope our men keep their cool and try to escape somehow, hopefully with the trucks and their cargo." Kees just nodded his head and said, "Who would have thought the Nazis would pull a trick like this; and then just before they lose the war? We need to find out who gave the order and planned this. We will have them charged with a war crime!

"We need to go to the Boxers' 'office' and discuss what we need to do next, and in particular, what to do tomorrow night. I am sure all the men who were in the field will come there. Perhaps, they will have some idea where the trucks have gone too." Frans was taking charge of the dilemma. "If anything, we cannot afford this to happen tomorrow night as well."

Leo was irate. He was so mad that he was shouting at everyone who entered the "office." When Kees and Frans came in, he began to take his anger out on them. "Who was it? Who gave you permission to get the trucks, Kees?"

Kees walked over to Leo and looked him straight in the eyes saying, " The airpórt commander made a phone call to Seiss Inquart, the Nazi Governor. I heard him ask the questions and after perhaps ten minutes of conversation he nodded his head, hung up the phone, and told me that we had the supreme commander's full cooperation. I had no reason to doubt him on that."

It was three a.m. when all the men who had been at the drop site, had arrived at the "office". After a quick headcount they were able to make a list of those who were missing. "Tomorrow," Leo announced, "I want two volunteers to go with me to Seiss Inquart. I also want at least twenty men to follow us and wait outside the office of Seiss until we come back out. If we don't return within the hour, burn the place!" Leo was still very mad and he did not hide it. Some men began to raise objections, but Leo silenced them with a wave of his hands. "Bear in mind, guys, Seiss is scared to death and wants to go home alive; he will do anything to appease us in these final days. I sincerely doubt that it was him who gave the order to steal our food and arrest our men."

Kees was the first one who volunteered to go with Leo. "I believe you are right in your surmise and I want to be the first to ask Seiss about it. If he does not know anything about this, we should ask him to prosecute the people who did this for the sake of his 'good name.'" His remark caused a lot of smiles in the audience, despite the grim occasion. The meeting was adjourned after all the men had been urged to stand by for the following evening, and a possible sccond food drop.

When most men had gone home, five men remained in the "office" – Kees and Frans in their function as leaders in the Resistance and Leo, Erick and Bart in their function as leaders of the Boxers. "You did not really mean to burn down the Ancient and Historical Binnenhof, did you?" Frans asked.

Leo shook his head. "People say a lot of things in their anger. No, realistically I would not dream of it." Kees took the initiative to bring up the issue of the food drop planned for the following night.

"I feel we need to notify England, immediately. We should let them decide what we should do next. A similar drop like the one last night is out of the question. Personally I think they should drop food all over the city. Not in crates but just in smaller boxes and preferably on small parachutes if such things exist. Our people need food now, and they cannot wait much longer because we want to 'organize' it efficiently."

A few days prior the Boxers had installed a radio transmitter in their "office". Leo led them to the equipment and began to transmit a message to London. It took only a minute to get an answer. "We are aware of the disaster which occurred last night." The men looked at each other in surprise.

"How can they know this already?" Kees uttered.

The voice from England continued, "Seiss Inquart himself has told us two hours ago and even he was irate about the incident, about which he said he know nothing of. He offered to have a full investigation tomorrow and promised to do anything in his power to find the culprits." The five listeners were flabbergasted. It slowly dawned on them that their difficult task of visiting Seiss Inquart would no longer be necessary.

It was Frans, the practical man, who thought aloud, "If it was not the leadership of the Nazis who had ordered the attack of the food convoy, who had? Perhaps we should pay a visit to the airport and talk to the commander there.

Can we have some fighting men to come with us to back us up?" He asked Leo. "We might even find our men there."

"Let's go take a nap and come back here at eight o'clock to discuss our options and do what we have to do." With those words Kees ended the meeting.

Chapter Thirty One

BLACK MARKET

—∞—

It was May 4, 1945. Rumors of the end of the war grew stronger by the day. City after city was freed from the oppressors. Other cities, that is. Not The Hague. It was frustrating to the Hagenaars.

Radio Oranje announced that morning, "The Americans have arrived at Rotterdam and taken the City, half in ruins, without any significant battle. The German Commander in Rotterdam ordered his soldiers to hand in their arms at the requested location and surrender to the demands of the Americans. Food drops will commence as planned. The citizens are requested to stay in their houses between the hours of two and four this afternoon, to prevent getting injured by the falling packages."

Kees and Frans were at the "office" early in the morning. The news of the morning had changed their plans. Leo was ready to visit Seiss Inquart. He had not heard the news yet, but when he was told about it, he remained determined to go. "If it is only to free our men. You know how the Gestapo is. They are permitted to shoot our men even at this last hour. We have to go for their sake." Hopefully Seiss was not involved in this.

"I agree with Leo," Frans said, "He has the power to find out who ordered the attack and get those involved brought in. They will be judged by the approaching Americans."

"I don't think we will need a back up at this stage. I bet Seiss is peeing his pants as it is," Leo remarked as the left their "office" for an hour's stroll to the Binnenhof.

What they saw on their way to the center of The Hague made them very angry. About three kilometers from the "office", they ran into a large crowd of people who were carrying boxes that looked like the ones they had loaded on the trucks the previous night at the airport. "Do you see what I see?" Frans asked. The three men tried to get through the crowd to the center of where the boxes were coming from. A warehouse, with four men in front of the open doors, was piled up with boxes and the men were selling them to the crowd. Their hands full of stacks of money, they negotiated with each person on a price. The three men looked at the scene and became angrier by the minute.

"Let them do their dirty job and sell out the rest of it. The people need the food; that is clear. Meanwhile we need to get out of here to the nearest police station and have these four guys arrested as soon as the crowd is gone. We don't want to create a riot as long as the people are here. Let's go!" Kees told the others.

The police station was only a block away. When they entered there were no more soldiers or Gestapo men as had been customary in the last five years.

The policeman in charge recognized Kees and asked, "What can we do for you, gentlemen?" The normally composed men began to speak, all three at the same time. The policeman raised his hand, "One at a time please. I can't hear a word from you if you behave like excited schoolboys. What is going on that has you so wound up?"

It was Leo who took the initiative to make a full report of their findings including the attack from the night before. "We must hurry to catch the four guys before they run off with all the money or we will never know who is behind all this criminal activity."

An hour later four men had been arrested. Boxes of money were confiscated, but that was useless to feed anyone at that time. Kees and Frans had witnessed the arrest and left the questioning of the culprits for later. Hopefully, soon after the war had ended. When that would be, no one could tell. Kees and Frans decided to go back home and dismiss the matter for the time being. Seiss Inquart would have to explain a lot of things. "Later," said Kees "justice will prevail and we will find out who was behind this crime."

Frans remarked, "I would not be surprised if these four thugs are NSB-ers doing their filthy work for a group of Nazis who thought they could go home with a bunch of money." This time the police did not have to get permission from the Nazis to lock up someone. The usual Gestapo men were nowhere to be seen!

When Kees came home, Johanna was dancing in the front room and singing, "Long live the Queen."

"Kees, it's over. The Queen came back today. She and the princesses have arrived at the Airport in Brabant and they are going to their palace in Soestdijk today. The war is over, Kees, it really is."

Kees shook his head, "Not here, yet. In fact there is a warning from the government to stay indoors and wait until the end of the war is officially announced by the government. As long as you see German soldiers walking around on the streets, we are at war. I don't want to dampen your joy, Johanna, but please be realistic."

Cornelius had heard the warning and asked, "Can I go play outside so I can tell my friends what you just said, Dad?"

"Yes you can, son, but be careful. Anything can still happen." In the street it seemed like everything had changed. Groups of people were talking about peace. It is over. Finally the Nazis have surrendered.

The Americans will be here tomorrow. Someone brought a radio out into the street. The national Anthem sound crackling loudly in the street for everyone to hear, including the German soldiers who were walking through the streets and acting as if nothing had changed. This was a different kind of chaos. Just days before, the chaos was depressing; now it was exhilarating. Freedom, freedom! It's here and we will be staying alive to experience freedom. The reporter on the radio announced: "We are free at last." A deafening burst of cheering sounded through the street. People began to dance, give each other hugs. The sound of liberation came from hurt hearts and pained souls. Everyone was outside; everyone was talking to someone. They forgot about the Nazi soldiers who are still patrolling in the street.

One soldier took his uniform off, dropped his gun on the pile, then his helmet and in his underwear he went to the side walk. He dropped to his knees and began to cry, with a loud voice and through his tears he yelled: "Umsonst, alles wahr umsonst; Entschuldigung; Entschuldigung, Bitte."(It was all for naught, I am sorry.) The people were overwhelmed with joy, but seeing a crying soldier asking for forgiveness dampened the celebrations. It was amazing how many people had gathered in the street. Cornelius did not know there were that many people on his street.

All of a sudden, shots were fired. Is someone out of his mind? In seconds the street was empty again. The soldiers could no longer stand the celebrations and made an end to it by shooting in the air. It may be liberation for part of Holland, but not in The Hague, not just yet.

The BBC, Radio Oranje, announced that the Allieds had opened the gates of many concentration camps. What they saw there was horrible. People were dying while celebrating their liberation. Thousands could not even walk and had to be carried to the army vehicles that would take them to field hospitals.

The need for food for the freed prisoners was so great that the Allied forces ran out the same day they arrived. The Nazis had run days before, leaving the gates locked and in many camps the devastation and disorder was indescribable. Many of the liberating soldiers cried when they met the camp prisoners.

The Camp gates were opened.
The American flag is raised on the security arm.

On Saturday, the fifth of May, it really seemed to have happened! The American and Canadian armies had reached the west of the country. Because of that news, which was now freely available to the citizens in the big cities, the flags, long hidden, came out. Cornelius had never seen the flags and when he walked out into the street he could not believe his eyes. It was such a festive sight to behold that he ran quickly back to tell his mother. The population had been prepared for the liberation. Flags from several nations had been sewn together out of old sheets and dyed in the respective colors. Again everyone seemed to have taken to the streets, yet in between the crowds the "Moffen" were still patrolling the streets and they still carried arms. It was quite surreal.

The banners on the flags were orange, and everywhere one could see people wearing orange sashes or orange ribbons. The girls had orange bows in their hair. When Cornelius saw all the orange decorations, he ran back home again and told his mom that he would sell all the marigolds he could pick from his plants in the backyard. "My dear son," Johanna answered, "it is too early for marigolds."

"No mom, I have them in my little hothouse and there are a lot of them."

"But, son, listen to me carefully. The soldiers are still in the city, and as long as they are here we should not agitate them. Just wait a few more days. Besides," she argued persuasively, "you will have more of the marigolds by then."

The news reporter announced that the Germans were handing in their arms and their helmets, but in The Hague it was not happening. Soldiers had not received the "Befehl" from their commanders to quit. From time to time in the days following May 5, shots could be heard. People were still killed for the smallest misstep they would make and the regular policemen still did not have any authority.

Chapter Thirty Two

FREE, BUT STILL AT WAR

Henk de Groot, the fairly new Dominee de Groot, went to the city of Amersfoort to visit an internment camp which had been lead by Commander Kotaella. A Canadian regiment had chased away the Nazis and had given temporary management to the International Red Cross. The people in the camp had been advised to stay in the camp until the entire country had been cleared of the Nazis. The camp had been a halfway station from which people would be transferred to the death camps of Germany and Poland. Hundreds of recently uncovered Jews had been sent to this camp during the last sixty days of the war, and Henk had received a message to come and minister to those Jews.

The present leader of the camp, Mrs.Overeem, told him upon arrival that a rumor was circulating that the Nazis were coming back out of revenge and they were afraid that they would kill a number of the Jews and perhaps also some of the former associates who knew too much. They could testify of the lewd behavior of the former oppressors to the courts and cause them to be convicted of crimes.

"I have contacted the oxers, but they have not shown up yet; could you do something about that?" Mrs. Overeem implored. Henk promised her to see what he could do immediately. "Would you be willing to stay here tonight and give my people some encouragement?"

Henk agreed to that. "But, let me go and see if I can get in touch with the Boxers and hopefully I can get a number of them to come for the night."

Henk left and found one of his Resistance contacts who in turn notified the Boxers. He returned within an hour with fifteen Boxers. They now could carry guns openly and set up armed guards at the entrance.

Twice that night, a Nazi army truck stopped at the camp. They were chased away by the armed Boxers. No one ever knew what the Nazis would have done if it had not been for Henk's visit and his persistence with the Boxers. The next day a battalion of the Americans arrived at the city of Amersfoort; they took charge of the camp and arrested every German that came into their sight.

Henk continued his work for which he had come to the camp; the same way as he had before, by asking the Jews why the Christians had taken the risk to hide them. He was able to convert several Jews to Christianity. Over the next few days, some of them were able to go back to the cities they had been taken from. The Americans took up the difficult task of identifying all the people in the camp, including the workers. It appeared that many of the workers had been former collaborators with the enemy; most of those were now locked up in the camp, where they had formerly been watchmen and bullies to the innocent.

In every city, where the Allieds had defeated the Nazis, a committee of Resistance men, Boxers and regular Dutch army called "*Binnenlandse Strijdkrachten, B.S.* for short, was formed under leadership of the Americans. Their task was to bring order in the city, reveal the NSB-ers and collaborators and lock them up. Remaining Nazi soldiers and officers often found in hiding, were arrested and placed in a Prisoner of War camp. None of them were sent back to Germany until their record had been cleared.

People were warned to keep their German Ausweiss with them plus any ID which would prove their identity. It felt like the Nazi roadblocks had just been replaced by American roadblocks. The Americans were much friendlier, though, except when there was doubt about an identification. Most of the Resistance men had difficulty identifying themselves for who they really were. Often they had multiple identifications which purposely never matched.

Henk de Groot, formerly Rabbi Levi Strauss who had five different ID's, was stopped at an American roadblock on the way to The Hague for a visit with Kees and Johanna. When he showed his ID as Dominee Henk de Groot, the soldier looked at him suspiciously. "Do you have any other identification?" the M.P. asked.

"Yes, I do," Henk answered and showed him his ID as Rabbi Levi Strauss.

To his surprise the M.P. ordered him to sit on the ground and handcuffed him. "We have been warned to watch for imposters especially those who take on a Jewish role. It is impossible that a real Rabbi can still walk around freely in this country. They have all been sent to the concentration camps in Germany and Poland," the man patiently explained. "You will have to produce witnesses who will verify who you are. Until then you will be placed in custody." Henk shook his head in dismay when he was lead away to a waiting room.

The same day, Kees had a similar experience, but his was with a Nazi control unit. The Hague was still in the hands of the Germans, simply because the Americans had not taken over power from the Nazis. It would take three more days until the American and Canadian troops had enough manpower in the city to take full control.

It was a bright and clear sunny morning on the ninth of May in 1945 when the citizens on the streets of The Hague were abruptly disturbed on their early morning walks by the roar of innumerable airplanes. They seemed to be flying very low and unlike the planes which had dropped food before, these planes were flying in close formation. At once, by what seemed like a silent command, all the doors of the planes opened and thousands of parachutes unfolded almost in an instant. The clear, early morning sky looked like it had become cloudy as the white parachutes slowly descended. They landed everywhere – in back yards and on rooftops. At last, the long-awaited Americans had finally arrived.

Within hours the city was in the hand and power of the liberators and before they knew it, the Nazi soldiers were marching in large columns towards a quickly erected POW camp. Some of them seemed relieved, the most fanatic expressed their anger, and the older, routine-bound ones were complacent.

They had been expecting the end, but none of them had expected humane treatment. They had been too brainwashed to expect mercy from their enemies. The next day the committee for justice was formed and the hunt was on for the collaborators, the "moffenmeiden", and the NSB-ers. Many of them had disappeared and many more were in hiding, but with the help of the population they were all found and later tried in the Dutch courts.

Cornelius had a great time. Playing in the street all day, he saw a lot of the activities happening before his eyes. He felt part of the festivities. Together with his friends they danced and sang in the street. All of a sudden he heard loud screams and cries from one of the neighbor girls. She was pushed to the center of the street and many people surrounded her.

Parades and flowers everywhere.

Cornelius was watching the scene in horror. What were they doing to the nice girl who always had a friendly word for him? Each time the girl was pushed to the other side of the circle someone would pull on her clothes. The girl was sobbing, but the people around her were becoming meaner and nastier. The poor girl was almost naked and the scratches she had received began to bleed. Cornelius watched as two men were holding the girl while two other men were cutting of her beautiful long blonde hair. Cornelius began to cry; he could not bear it any longer and yelled as loud as he possibly could, "Stop! You mean people, stop! Don't you see, you are hurting the girl?" It was too much for the little boy who had experienced a war so intensely. Through his tears he yelled again, "Stop, stop!" The people did not listen and continued their unusual torture. Crying and completely distraught he ran home. Johanna saw him coming and wrapped her arms around him. He tried to explain what he had seen, but he could not. It had been too much for the boy.

Johanna rocked him for a while and then she began to explain, "The sweet girl, who was treated that way had been very naughty." She said, "She had done things that had been against the citizens and she had acted like a sort of NSB-er. The neighbors were taking out their anger against her and that was wrong, too. I think they have stopped now, I saw police coming while you ran inside. I hope they rescued her."

"I hope so, too," Cornelius uttered still sobbing.

Kees came home exhausted, an hour after the incident. Cornelius tried to tell him what he had seen in the street, but he could not. The minute he began, he cried instead. Kees took the boy on his knee and announced, "I have some great news for you two. Tomorrow your brothers and sister are coming home. I just received a message from the station that they expect the children to arrive at three o'clock."

There were no telephones, communication was simply word of mouth, but that afternoon most of the parents were at the station. They were waiting with great anticipation for their children who had been able to, more or less, escape the severity of the war. The train from the north country of the Netherlands, the provinces of Friesland and Groningen, was late. Nothing worked on time in those days. More importantly a great surprise was awaiting the city of The Hague. A long train arrived first and unloaded thousands of Dutchmen who had been arrested during the previous years and who had been shipped to Germany as slave laborers. Their unexpected arrival was cause for a huge ovation from the waiting parents. Mothers who saw their sons again after three years and wives who saw their husband were crying with joy. They had almost forgotten the real reason why they were at the station. It was a great day of homecoming that thirteenth day of May 1945.

Trainloads of slave laborers came back from captivity.
Equally as many did not return.

Chapter Thirty Three

FREEDOM AND SHORTAGES

The freedom, which the Americans had finally brought to the country, and lastly to the city of The Hague, practically caused anarchy at first. The offices at the Binnenhof were found to be ransacked and the administrations of the cities had been destroyed. Many volunteers were put to work to restore and clean up municipal buildings and administrations. It led to complete confusion and disorder. The American soldiers did more than was expected from them, particularly in the reorganization of order and the prevention of calamities. The ruins which had been caused by the German bombs had to be fenced off and traffic had to be regulated. It seemed as if the entire population was on the streets. People who had been confined to their houses loved the freedom of walking outside. Traffic was practically only from the American army vehicles, some skinny horses which had survived the war and the looting by the departing Nazis.

Thousands of American soldiers were assisting the Resistance men in sorting out the good citizens from the bad. The police force had remained during the war, albeit under the supervision of the Nazis. Many police men had become collaborators to save their jobs. A small number had played a double role and supported the Resistance.

It was most difficult to separate the bad cops out. Frans and Kees and several other Resistance leaders were appointed to the task. Together with a group of Army interrogators each police man was interviewed and too often the policeman was arrested upon the advice of the Resistance men.

Kees came home exhausted every night. "It is so hard to accuse someone who has worn the uniform of the law in the last five years and then to find out the person did it only for himself. There is nothing worse than a crooked policeman who betrays the people he has a duty to protect." Kees lamented to Johanna when he sat down for dinner.

The family had been restored completely. Cornelius had a hard time adjusting to the divided attention he now received. "I am going to decorate the neighbors' horse and carriage for the parade tomorrow and I need to go to the Brandwijk farm to get a lot of marigolds. Can we go there tomorrow, dad?"

"No son, I have to work tomorrow, but Saturday I can."

"But Dad, the parade is on Saturday," Cornelius answered.

"Ask one of your brothers or your sister to go to the farm with you. It is only two hours to walk. They might like the trip which we have made so many times."

The next morning they went, Cornelius and the sister he hardly knew. On the way down they had a great time getting to know each other. They were tired from the long walk, but once at the farm they had a royal dinner, one like they both had not had for years and after several hours of roaming the farm Marie helped him pick marigolds. Arms full of them, until they realized it was too much to carry them back to the city on a second two hour walk. Farmer Brandwijk noticed the hesitation of the two children and offered a solution. "I will bring you to the city on the brick (a small horse drawn buggy which was used by the farmers to do errands).

Every city and every community had festivities. It was as if all creativity had been stored up for the liberation. For weeks, parties, parades and shows drew the attention of the citizens. Thus they were able to forget the troubles from the past. In the Deiman Straat and the adjacent streets, a parade had been organized, which would be followed by games and competitions.

All the children were involved in decorating bicycles, perambulators, and anything that could roll would qualify. Cornelius had talked to the neighbor Mr. Groenendijk who had some of his box bicycles returned to him by the Dutch police after the Nazis had left. Cornelius had asked his older brother to help him decorate the vehicle with the bright orange marigolds from the farm and from his own back yard. They placed the flowers between the spokes of the wheels and all around the edge of the box. When it was all done, Cornelius had asked his mother to make him an American Soldier uniform with a cap and a big star on it. In the parade his brother was riding the bicycle while Cornelius was standing in the box part, between all the orange flowers. On a piece of cardboard from a box they had found they wrote, *Thank you Amerikanen voor onze Vrijheid* (Thank you Americans for our freedom).

The day of the parade was a beautiful spring day. Flags waved everywhere and hundreds of people were standing on the sidewalk to watch the parade. Whenever they saw Cornelius' decorated box bicycle, the people applauded, while Cornelius saluted, like a real soldier.

Cornelius had to adjust to the new living situation at home. He missed going down under the floor and talking to the guests. Life in the house on the Deiman Straat was much busier with his two brothers and a sister at home. The schools were still closed and were not going to restart until September.

There were other changes, too. Kees was getting paid by the government for his work in reorganizing the administration and for being a member fo the tribunal that sorted out the good and the bad. Also, the news was more readily spread in the form of radio broadcasts. A warehouse with hundreds of thousands of radios was found. The Nazis had requisitioned them earlier in the war and apparently forgotten about them. One of the news reporters had stumbled onto them when they reopened the warehouse where once the inventory for the newspaper had been stored. He wrote an article in his paper about his find and the next morning thousands of citizens were waiting in line to pick up their lost treasure.

It was amazing how quickly the presses of the newspapers had been back in production. Some of the presses had been used by the Nazis, others had been closed down and never touched again until a day after the liberation. The paper had to be brought in from England. The only mill which made paper had been burned down by the Resistance in the second year of the war. Four newspapers had survived the war as illegal papers. They were the ones who had hand printed the illegal papers on little hand presses from hiding places often in the bombed out ruins.

(translation)
Four years of illegal war papers, now daily liberation news

The underground press comes above ground, four major papers emerge.

In the backyard, Cornelius' little farm still thrived. In the fall he had planted some strawberry plants. Marie told him what to do with the runners that grew on the plants in August. His little patch of strawberries had grown out to fifty plants and at the end of May he had picked his first strawberry. Ceremoniously he brought it to the dinner table that evening. His brothers and sister had laughed about his little farm but when they saw the big red strawberry he brought in they were amazed and praised him for his pending harvest. Johanna was given the honor of eating the strawberry, which she did very graciously.

Shortages of everything seemed to get even worse and people were selling anything to get money for food which was gradually, but sparsely coming back to the stores. Even if one did have money, it was difficult to purchase anything. The monetary situation was slowly getting better, but the merchants did not have much to sell. The seed store, where they sold feed and flower and vegetable seeds, had run out of its supply in three days. Cornelius had gone to the store by himself to see what kinds of seed he could purchase for his little backyard farm. With his little coin wallet he had pleaded for some seeds. "I have money," he assured the merchant, "is there anything you can sell me, sir?"

The merchant shook his head and replied, "I will get some in soon, but I don't know what is coming or when it's coming in."

Cornelius shook his head and remarked precociously, "What is this country coming to? Now we are free and there is still nothing to buy. I will have to go to the farms to get what I need."

As he was leaving the store, the merchant called after him, "I have some fertilizer."

Cornelius answered, "That is the only thing I don't need," shaking his head.

At home he asked Johanna, "When can dad take me to the Brandwijk farm? I need seeds and young plants for the summer. The store has nothing for sale and if they have no supplies soon, I will not be able to fill the space in the yard."

Johanna understood his sense of urgency. He had grown up in lack and expected it to continue forever. "I will ask dad when he comes home, tonight. He needs some time off anyway and going to the farm might be a great diversion from his hectic schedule."

A new phenomenon was emerging in the war-torn country of The Netherlands. The many liberators had some free time, at night and on the weekends. They went to parties, shows and games and met the Dutch girls. The young men and women had been starved for affection, the soldiers having been on the battle grounds and the Dutch girls stuck in the curfew. The girls were grateful to the soldiers, and the brave men of the armed forces were charmed by the Dutch blondes. From both sides there were open doors to be together. It resulted in many quick marriages and, nine months later, thousands of babies were born without knowing their fathers.

The administrative tasks from these marriages appeared to be enormous. Often the girls had no birth records of themselves because the local administration had been burned by the parting Nazis. The Troops had to get their birth certificates from their home towns in America or Canada and the postal system was very slow and erratic. Yet thousands of marriages were performed. Later some marriages had to be dissolved while other couples were separated for a long time. The soldiers had two options – either bring their bride home to America, or Canada, or come back for them later. Some decided to remain in The Netherlands.

Most weddings were celebrated in a big way! "Anything to have a party," was the motto. Flowers were provided from the back yards and put together by the mother of the bride. Wine was brought in from France and Dutch beer was readily available again.

Many Canadian and American soldiers married Dutch girls. Many babies were born with an American "Daddy."

Chapter Thirty Four

VICTORIOUS REUNION

Towards the end of May most of the Jews who had been in hiding were coming home to their own houses. In almost all cases they found their homes completely ransacked and anything of value had been robbed by either the Nazis or the NSB-ers. Many of the Jews were happy to be home even if it was empty. They were grateful to have survived the Holocaust. Many of them had nothing but the clothes they wore. A few had possessions stashed away in their own homes. There was a spirit of sharing among them. Those who had shared what they had with others. It was in that spirit that a group of over two hundred came together in a school building that had survived the bombing.

These people had gone through the most severe times in their lives, but they had two things in common – they all went through Kees and Johanna's hiding place in the Deiman Straat and they all new Rabbi Levi Strauss. The reunion was not complete without those three people. One thankful refugee offered to see if he could get them to come the following evening. They all agreed to bring some food and drinks and decided to be back in the same location the following evening. "Don't forget the little boy! He has done so much for us, too,"Old Mr. Abraham Feinsmith remarked.

That same evening Kees heard a soft knock on the door. "Who can that be at this hour?" he inquired of Johanna. "My heart still jumps a beat when I hear a knock without knowing who could be there."

"Don't worry Kees, the war is really over and the Gestapo guys are either in jail or in a prisoner-of-war camp. Let's see who brings us the honor of a visit tonight." Without hesitation Johanna opened the door. Her voice sounded with great surprise, "Rabbi Levi Strauss, oh, what a pleasant surprise to see you. We were just talking about you and wondered when you would finally show up in the city." Johanna kept chattering while she pulled Levi inside and literally pushed him into a chair. "Where have you been, in the last three weeks?"

"Shalom to you and your family." He stood up and gave both Kees and Johanna a hug. "I have been busy identifying the Jewish people who came out of hiding. You probably know that they did not have much by which to be identified, and I have been asked to help the Americans with this difficult task. Fortunately, I know practically all of them and because of that most of them have been allowed to go to their houses here in the city."

"I have been doing similar work," Kees remarked, "not with the Jews, mind you, but with practically the entire population of the city. It is amazing how many NSB-ers we caught. It proves that hunger and lack can change peoples' hearts and turn them into traitors, just to survive. Alas, they are going to have to pay for their choices."

They had a lot to talk about. Time flew by and when the clock chimed twelve times, Levi asked, "I guess I should have asked you earlier, can I stay here for the night?"

"Of course, Levi, you are our brother in Christ and even if you were not, we would still prepare a bed for you right now."

They were having breakfast when the doorbell rang. It was one of those real bells which connected to a spring, which in turn tied to the bell with a steel wire. Outside was a square brass knob and if you pulled to too hard, it would make the bell ring very loud. This had happened to the man outside and he was a little embarrassed and apologetic when Kees opened the door. Kees recognized the man right away, but he did not remember the man's name.

Kees did not acknowledge that he did not remember the person's name and said, "Well I'll be, if it is not, eh…"

"David Gouds," the man filled in.

"What a great blessing to see you, safe and well. Come on inside. I believe we already have a visitor who will also be happy to see you." The two men walked the short hallway to the front room.

David showed his surprise by letting out a big sigh, "Goodness gracious, the man I have been looking for is here of all places."

David had been at the van Rijn residence as one of the first fugitives. It was he who had volunteered to invite the family to the Jewish reunion. "Rabbi Levi, how are you, sir? I have been asking around to find out if anyone knew where you were, and now I ran into you. That is great! We would like to celebrate the liberation tonight, together with some people you all know. I have taken the chore to find you and invite you."

Kees finally remembered the man. He was a doctor who, at the very beginning of the war, was working at the hospital. He had been told by a wounded officer he was treating, that the Jewish people were being deported and that doctors would be first on the Nazi hit list because they were needed in Germany. The officer was mutilated for life. He would never fight again. Out of gratefulness to the doctor who saved his life he had warned him to disappear immediately.

So Doctor David Gouds had asked his Rabbi, Levi Strauss, where he could go underground for a little while. The Rabbi had given him the van Rijn address. At the time they had only four guests and most people had been brought to a farm quickly in order to make room for the many others who could be expected. Several times Levi had visited the farm where David had been for three years. He had been surprised that David had never been asked to go to England as so many doctors had. And here he was, alive and well ready to help build the country back up. He was a man of few words, who did not really like to talk and when Kees asked him about his three years of hiding he shook his head and said, "I have washed the entire episode out of my mind. I will never talk about it again."

Kees and Johanna asked him where the reunion was going to be held and at what time and agreed to be there. "What about you, Rabbi Levi? Will you come too?"

Levi nodded his head and answered him, "Yes, I will, but will there be a chance for me to speak to the audience?"

"I will make sure you can, sir." David stood up and walked to the door saying, "Thank you, shalom. I will see you tomorrow," and left.

"Dad, please come, the shack is falling down. I almost got hit by the sidewall," Cornelius called from the backdoor. It sounded very urgent, so Kees ran to the backyard to find the shack hanging over, almost hitting the ground. There used to be a wooden fence behind it, but during the last winter they had systematically broken down the fence. Sharing the wood with the neighbor, they had used up the entire fence for the desperately needed fuel in the wood burning stove to cook whatever they had scrounged up and needed to cook.

The fence had partly supported the shack which was now ready to completely cave in. They both looked at the mess and Kees wondered what it would take to repair the very much needed storage. He decided he would have to buy two 8 foot poles to support the structure. He would have to get help to push the wall back in place. He needed nails to nail the whole thing back together.

"Well, son, are you ready to go with me to the hardware store?"

Cornelius nodded his head and said, "Sure, dad, I'd love to go with you. I have missed our little trips lately. Yes, let's go." They mounted the legendary bicycle which had been part of their Resistance and Kees rode the two miles to the hardware store.

Mr. Boskamp, the owner of the store shook his head sadly and announced, "I can sell you two poles, Kees, and I can have those delivered this afternoon, but nails, I don't have. Not one nail or screw in the store. Everyone has been repairing something or boarding up places and the Nazis took everything with them to Germany when they left. They looted the store and took all they could carry on their vehicles. My supplier is still shut down and I have no idea where to get nails."

They left and while they rode back home, Cornelius had an idea. At home he asked his dad for his claw hammer. A year ago he had seen his dad pull out old nails from the scrounged up wood. He had played in one of the ruins down the street, even though it was forbidden, and he had seen lots of nails sticking out of the mangled wooden floors. He was determined to bring his dad a handful of nails. Kees did not ask what his plan was with the claw hammer. Cornelius' mind was surprisingly enterprising.

At the end of the morning, the boy came back. In his little hand he had a bunch of nails. Rusted but strait, the nails were useable. Proudly, like a cat presenting his catch, he laid them on the table in front of Kees and declared, "Here are your nails, Dad. This time you don't have to pay for them, but if you need more, they will cost you ten cents each."

They all laughed, and Levi remarked: "I can see you have Jewish blood, Cornelius. You will become rich in the future."

"It is a very tough job, you know, and I hit my fingers several times, but I am tough too. From now on, I am going to pull nails everyday and I will become so good at it that I can sell them to everyone who needs them, for ten cents each of course." Wisely he repeated what was known to be posted over the entrances of the Nazi labor camps, *"Arbeit Adelt."* They all laughed again, where did this little boy get all his wisdom?

He went back to the ruins after lunch and brought home more nails. "These are not for you, Dad. I promised them to Mr. Boskamp at the hardware store and he is willing to pay me ten cents each, every time I have some."

It was late in the afternoon, when the family was getting ready to go to the greatly anticipated party with the Jewish people. Only Kees and Johanna were going and they were taking Cornelius because he had asked if he could come. "I know a lot of those people," he had pleaded, "and I would like to see them again. Please let me come." They had agreed.

"But there will be a lot of things discussed which you may not understand," Johanna had warned him.

The three adults and Cornelius walked to the old school at six thirty. To their great surprise it seemed like no one was there until they entered the door of the old, partly caved in, gymnasium.

For years, they had not seen that many Jews together, yet most of them they had hosted in their humble home, underneath the floor at the Deiman Straat. The people came to Kees and Johanna and hugged and kissed them as though they were their long lost parents. Cornelius stood back a little; all that *schmooching* was not his cup of tea. Some of the friends with whom he had talked a lot, attempted to hug him, but he avoided it as much as he could.

At last, after all the greeting had passed, everyone sat down. There were no chairs in the building, the old wooden school benches had been burned in the stoves of the neighborhood, but most of those people present had brought a blanket to sit on. Kees looked over the crowd and counted more than two hundred and twenty heads. He had never counted the number of people they had hidden. Was it that many? Or even more? A few minutes later he would find out!

In the middle of the group, they had built a podium of boxes they had found in the basement of the school. The people all faced the make shift podium when David Gouds came forward. He welcomed all the people and mentioned the unique opportunity he had encountered when he had found Levi Strauss at the van Rijn residence. "I would have never thought he would be there when I went to invite Kees and Johanna." They all applauded. "I especially welcome Kees and Johanna, here tonight. We all have reason to thank them for saving our lives, for coping with us when we were bored and scared underneath their floor. A place where the crack board sounded too many times a day."

They all laughed, "Where we all could sing and even worship Jahweh in their most inventive creation, the singing box." They did not laugh this time. This was becoming serious talk. David continued, "Where we could have mature conversations with their wise, little son Cornelius who was often able to give us consolation and hope." Cornelius shrunk into his little corner, but when David asked, "Cornelius, would you please stand up? Thank you." He could not refuse to do so. With tears in his eyes he looked around into all those familiar faces and realized they loved him, and he love them! A thundering applause sounded for him. He quickly sat down, embarrassed.

David summed up all the things that had happened to him after he had been brought to a permanent hiding place at a farm. After his story, many others followed him, all telling, what by now sounded like adventures but what had really been their personal nightmare. After two hours of intense talking and listening, David announced, "We are taking a break for one hour. We have drinks and food in the next room. After we come back we can have some more speakers. I hope you are all enjoying this evening in honor of the van Rijn family."

If a Jewish family invites people for dinner, the word "dinner" is too simple for what has been set before the quests. When two hundred Jews create a dinner it turns out to be the most elaborate feast, as was the case at this reunion. While they were enjoying the food and the fellowship, many people came to Kees and Johanna and thanked them personally for what they had meant to them. Cornelius had the time of his life. He had never seen so much food from which he could choose whatever he liked. Time flew by and as if it seemed ten minutes, the hour of eating had passed.

Every one returned to their place on the floor in the gymnasium and as soon as they were seated, the oldest man of the group came to the makeshift podium and began to speak. "Instead of having more stories, let us celebrate the rest of this evening with a word from our friend and hero, our own Rabbi Strauss." A lengthy standing ovation brought Levi to the podium. After the applause died down, the Rabbi raised his hands and with a steady voice he began.

"Praise the Lord for all of you, being able to attend this meeting and having been given a new lease on life." Several people raised an eyebrow when he spoke Christian words instead of the usual Jewish greeting. "Some of you I have spoken to during the past six months, but many I have not seen for a longer time. I have told my story to only half of you here present, and I want to share it again, this time with all of you. I have a number of reasons to tell you about my experience, but the biggest reason is because of the two people you are honoring here tonight: Kees and Johanna van Rijn." Every one stood up, faced Kees and Johanna, and applauded.

He waited for the applause to end and when the people were seated again, he continued. "We could ask Kees and Johanna why they were able to do what they did during the entire length of the war. I know the answer and most of you do, too. I would like to urge you here and now to embrace that reason." Some of the people looked puzzled and began to shift uncomfortably. Others were shaking their heads and several shouted, "Preach it, brother!"

Levi took a deep breath and began to tell his story, how he had wondered why Dutch citizens were protecting and hiding the Jews. "I asked myself why they did it. Every time I visited a hiding place, a farm or a city home, I studied the people who took the biggest risks to help our people. I ask you all right now like I have asked many Jews in the last four months, what motivated them?" He took a few minutes to let it sink in. It was dead silent in the room. Then several people raised their hands and Levi noticed those with hands raised were people who had told him that they had accepted Jesus in their lives.

"I don't ask anyone to tell me why, because that is a very personal matter. I will tell you all why, because I, a Jewish Rabbi; I would have never thought I would ever come to this conclusion. But, I did and that is why I cannot call myself a Jewish Rabbi anymore." Several people were visibly shocked about the statement. A number of women gasped and held their hands to their mouth. Were they thinking that he committed blasphemy? "What all those families had in common was the very thing we as Jews have rejected for almost two thousand years. They all answered my question 'why', with 'Jesus gave us the strength.'" Addressing Kees and Johanna he asked them, "Am I right about that?"

Both nodded their heads, and Kees stood up and announced it out loud. "Without Jesus we could have never done it. We would all have died of hunger, or would have been arrested and sent to the Death camps. Yes, we were supernaturally protected by the name of Jesus whom we all confess to be our Lord and Savior."

No one spoke, no one dared to say a word. They all were thinking, what is coming next? There was a pregnant pause before Levi spoke again: "I too have accepted Jesus as my Lord and Savior and I know there are at least ten people here in this place who have, as well, simply because they have seen the evidence of the power of Jesus in their lives. I would like to end my talk with a prayer. Please bow your heads and close your eyes. While no one is looking around, please repeat after me." The Rabbi prayed "The Sinner's Prayer" and asked those who meant it, to raise their hands. "Please listen to what the Holy Spirit tells you to do." A large number did raise their hands and when Levi told them to look up he saw a lot of eyes glistening with tears of joy. "I would like to talk to those who have raised their hands and I will do that in private after this evening of celebration is over." With those words he ended and sat down.

Chapter Thirty Five

THE GIFT

Three of the Jewish young men walked out of the room and when they returned, they carried a huge box. David came back to the podium and asked Kees and Johanna to come forward. Kees whispered to Johanna behind his hand, "Oh, no, I don't feel liking speaking. We have been mentioned too many times already." They went forward anyway as the entire crowd stood up and greeted them with thunderous applause. David announced; "Ladies and Gentlemen, in the book of Ester chapter six, verse two, it reads: *The king, whose life had been saved from murder asked; "What honor has been bestowed* (on the man) *for this?"* and the servant answered: "Nothing has been done for him." You all know the rest of the story and we all feel that we should honor Kees and Johanna and Cornelius as well, Cornelius where are you? They all looked around and finally out of the far corner of the room Cornelius stood up. Come forward, my little friend, you are just as much a part of this as your parents."

The three of them, the major members of the van Rijn family who had helped so many Jews, and saved so many lives, stood there, overwhelmed by the love which radiated from the crowd. Once more they all applauded adding shouts of, "We love you, Kees and Johanna. We love you, Cornelius, Thank you, thank you, thank you!"

When it quieted down, David declared, "Kees, Johanna, and Cornelius, we thank you and honor you with all our hearts and we will be forever grateful for what you have done for our people. This box and what is in it, is a token of our gratefulness, just a token, mind you. Everyone is this room has put a personal gift in this box, from whatever they still owned, for you and your family. We all did what we could under the circumstances. Please accept our gratitude." The crowd rose again and applauded once more. This time Kees raised his hand and asked them to give him a moment to say a word or two.

A reverent hush fell over the room. Kees waited a long time before he could speak. With tears in his eyes and swallowing hard he began, "What, my dear friends, can I say to such an avalanche of love and thanksgiving. What we have done was not out of our goodness, or braveness. If it were not for Jesus in our lives and the Biblical commandment, to love each other, and the words in Isaiah 62 verses 1 to 7, *For Zion's sake*, we would have never been able to have the guts and the strength to bring this task of saving lives, especially Jewish lives, to this point. Like your Rabbi said before, in His strength only, could this have been fulfilled. We have prayed daily for your safety, for food to feed you and even after you left our home, we continued to pray for you.

"The fact that you are alive today is only because of Jesus. To us, that is our great reward. Therefore, I have one urgent message for you, consider that a gift from me to you. By confessing that Jesus is your personal Savior, this entire war had a purpose." There was not one dry eye in the room.

EPILOGUE

After the war had ended, it took the country of The Netherlands many years to get back on its feet. Many nations gave financial and physical assistance and rebuilding began soon after the liberation. Rebuilding occurred in the family way as well as hundreds of Dutch girls married American soldiers and many babies were born nine months later with names like Bill, Joe and Jerry.

However, Cornelius grew up with great lack in his younger years. The city children were generally malnourished. Many diseases and plagues followed the war. Louse infestations, and contagious diseases were rampant. Inoculations had not become readily available. Surrounded by ruins everywhere, the children found places to play, even though the ruins were barricaded for up to five years. For at least a year, Cornelius went to school in wooden shoes he had received from his beloved Marie Brandwijk. She had become involuntarily pregnant by a German soldier just before the war ended. The soldier left and she never saw him again.

The ruins in the cities became more dangerous as time went on for at least two reasons – rapid deterioration and rat infestations, which of course brought more disease to the population.

Cornelius continued in his self chosen career of gardening and working with flowers. He is still alive and became a world travelling horticulturist. He worked with many countries developing floral industries.

Kees died in 1997 at the age of ninety seven and Johanna passed in 2003 at the old age of one hundred three. All Cornelius' brothers are still alive. Only one of his two sisters died in 2004.

Most of the collaborators, the feared NSB-ers, including Baron van Boetselaer were arrested in the months following the end of the war. They were tried and sentenced, some for as long as twenty years of imprisonment.

THE END OF PART TWO

BIOGRAPHY OF DIRK VAN LEENEN

—∞—

Dirk was born in 1940 just after the war had begun in The Netherlands. He is married to Cynthia June van Leenen. Together they had seven children. Presently they have five children. Two daughters passed away from cancer in 2009 and 2005 respectively. They have twenty grandchildren. Dirk is determined to educate the American youth about the years of the Holocaust. He does so by talking in schools and churches and anywhere else he is asked to speak.

They live in Arizona. Dirk has spent his life working with flowers as a horticulturist. He has several degrees in Horticulture and Floral Design. In addition to writing books he is presently involved as CEO in Palms for Healing, a company which researches the medical properties of the fruits from palm trees.

His interest in English literature began when he was still living in Holland. At the University of Leiden he studied English while he worked as an English instructor at Mercatus College in Rotterdam.

For years he used to tell stories about his experiences during the Second World War in Holland. His children and grandchildren always urged him to write a book about those difficult times. Since Dirk's mother was Jewish, his parents were actively involved in hiding Jews.

It was out of his parents stories, Dirk's own memories, stories from Holocaust survivors and from interviews with now elderly surviving Resistance members that he was able to write this book.

Dirk's motto is: *Lest we forget!*

Ode to the American Armed Forces

"Let us not forget"

A song, by Jeffrey Allen

A soldier in the Great War
In the south of France
As he battles in the trenches
He wonders, "How long can we last?"
As Pershing pushes onward
He bites back on the pain
If this is our final stand
It won't be in vain

Off the shores of Normandy
In the summer of '44
As we roll up on the beach head
We know what's in store
So we muster up our courage
And we take hold of our guns
We say a prayer, think of our wives
And up the beach we run

Let us not forget
The ones who sacrifice
Who fight for freedom
No matter what the price
So we can live our lives
A nation under God
For that we are in debt
Let us not forget

In the mountains of Korea
And the jungles of Vietnam
Our sons and brothers left as boys
But quickly became men
Many lost their innocence
And many more their lives
Let us not forget
What was purchased for that price

Let us not forget
The ones who sacrifice
Who fight on for the freedom
No matter what the price
So we can live our lives
A nation under God
For that we are in debt
Let us not forget

Now they fight in deserts
Among the blowing sands
Terrorists and roadside bombs
Are the threats that they withstand
But let there be no question
The goal is still the same
The blood they shed and lives they lose
Are all in freedom's name

Let us not forget
The ones who sacrifice
Who fight on for the freedom
No matter what the price
A nation under God
For that we are in debt
Let us not forget
So we can live our lives

Names of cities, rivers and provinces in Holland mentioned in this book, see map.

Provinces
a. Noord Holland
b. Zuid Holland
c. Zeeland
d. Brabant
e. Utrecht
f. Friesland

Rivers
G. Schelde
H. Rijn
I. Oude Rijn
J. De Vliet

Cities
1. Alphen
2. Amersfoort
3. Arnhem
4. Bergen op Zoom
5. Bodegraven
6. Breda
7. Den Haag
8. Delft
9. Eindhoven
10. Hoekse Waard
11. Leiden
12. Leidschendam
13. Mariendal
14. Utrecht
15. Oosterbeek
16. Oegstgeest
17. Oosterbeek
18. Oud Beirland
19. Raalte
20. Rhenen
21. Rijswijk
22. Soestdijk
23. Terneuzen
24. Tiel
25. Tilburg
26. Wageningen

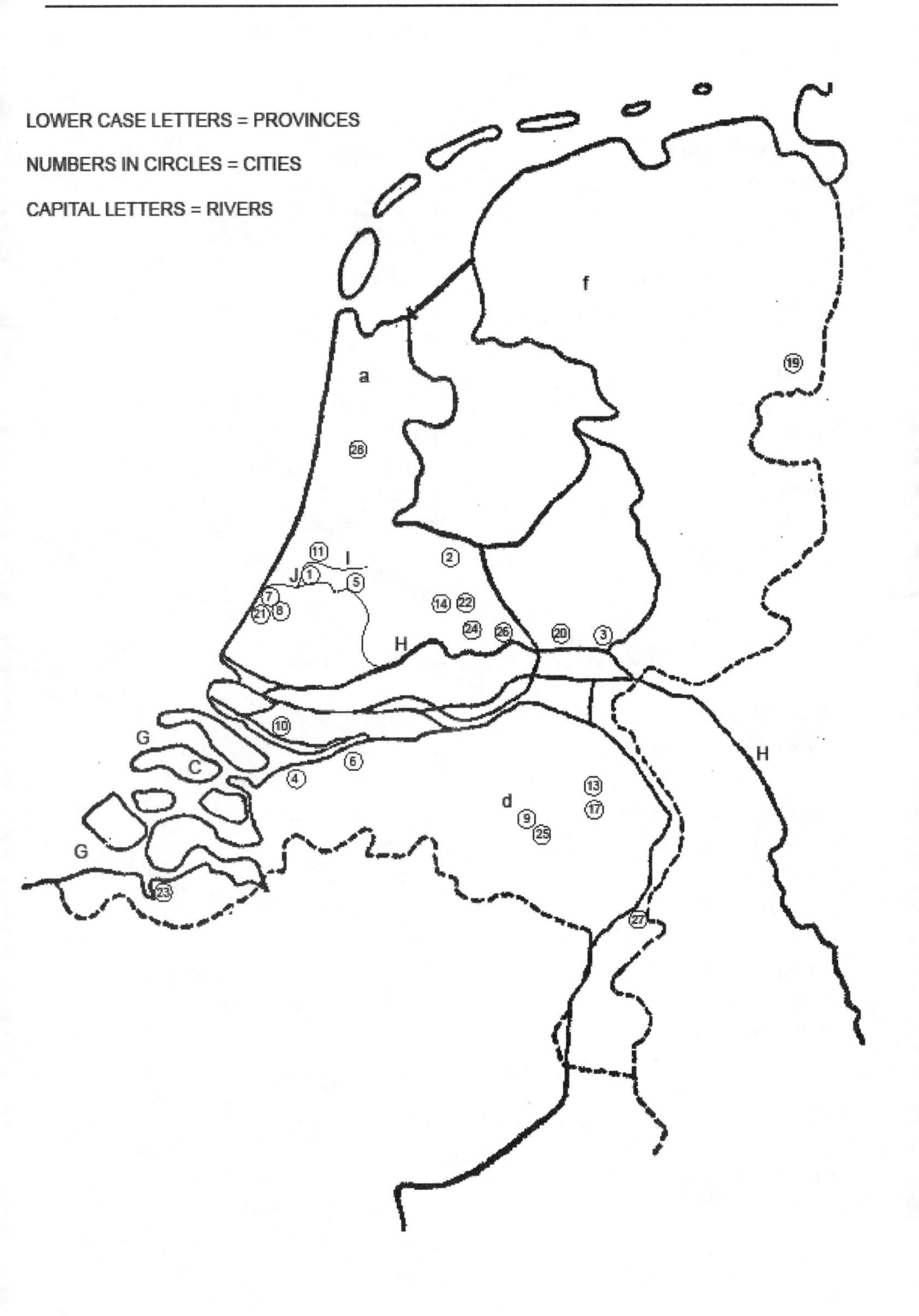

LOWER CASE LETTERS = PROVINCES
NUMBERS IN CIRCLES = CITIES
CAPITAL LETTERS = RIVERS
f
a
19
28
11
I
2
J
1
5
7
14
22
21
8
24
26
20
3
H
G
10
C
6
4
H
13
d
17
9
25
G
23
27

Glossary of Dutch Words and Expressions

Geestelijke	Clergy
Dominee	Minister /Pastor
Hervormde Kerk	Reformed church
Altijd honger	Always hungry
Surro	Surrogate/Artificial coffee
Vlaamse Reus	A large white rabbit
Binnenlandse Strijdkrachten (BS)	Local army/Reserves
NSB-er	Dutch member of The Socialistic Movement/ Traitor
Standrecht	Marshall law
Waterbaas	A Merchant who boils water
Moffen/ Moffies	Krauts/ German soldiers
Moffen meiden	Dutch girls who entertained Nazis
Ridderzaal	Meeting rooms of the Knights, Official Government assembly room
Radio Oranje	Radio Orange Named after the House of Orange. (The Royal Family)

Glossary of German Words and Expression

Ausweiss	German issued I.D. card
Wass ist loss mit Ihm ?	What is the matter with him?
Einem Moment bitte	Just a moment please
Gehen zu Hause, schnell	Go home quickly
Arbeitz Einsatz	Forced labor
Waffen SS	Armed security forces
Siecherheits Polizei	Security police
Heimat	Homeland
Befehl ist Befehl	A command is a command
Aufmachen schnell	Open up immediately
Leider Nieghts	Alas,nothing
Lass mahl gehen	Just let them go

Glossary of Jewish Words and Expressions

Shalom Shabbath	The peace of the Sabbath
Sjema Jisrael	Hear Israel, God is our lord, Jaweh is the only one
Jeshua	Jesus